THE TIMES TOP 100 GRADUATE EMPLOYERS

The definitive guide to the leading employers
recruiting graduates during 2009-2010.

HIGH FLIERS

HIGH FLIERS PUBLICATIONS LTD
IN ASSOCIATION WITH THE TIMES

Published by High Fliers Publications Limited
King's Gate, 1 Bravingtons Walk, London N1 9AE
Telephone: 020 7428 9100   Web: www.Top100GraduateEmployers.com

Editor Martin Birchall
Publisher Gill Thomas
Production Manager Robin Burrows
Portrait Photography Sarah Merson

Printed and bound in Italy by L.E.G.O. S.p.A.

A CIP catalogue record for this book
is available from the British Library.
ISBN 978-0-9559257-0-2

Contents

Employer Entries

Information Request Service
Find out more about Britain's top employers and you could
win a £50 iTunes voucher or start your career £5,000 richer!

Foreword

by Martin Birchall
Editor, The Times Top 100 Graduate Employers

W elcome to the latest edition of *The Times Top 100 Graduate Employers*, your guide to the UK's leading employers who are recruiting graduates in 2009-2010.

If you're one of the 320,000 final year university students due to graduate in the summer of 2010, then the latest employment outlook appears to be a little more encouraging than it has been. Whilst the 'Class of 2009' faced one of the most difficult job markets for a decade, there are signs that the graduate job market may be beginning to improve. Employers featured within the *Top 100* expect to hire 5.5 per cent more new recruits during the 2009-2010 recruitment season than last year, the first time since 2007 that the number of graduate jobs has increased year-on-year.

This may seem like a rather modest increase in opportunities but it is worth remembering that despite all the difficulties the recession has caused, at least 600 major employers in the UK have continued to operate a graduate recruitment scheme. For most of these, hiring new graduates is about developing a steady supply of future managers and leaders for their organisation, rather than simply filling immediate vacancies.

Few leading employers are keen to break this essential talent pipeline and so – irrespective of the economic conditions – most are maintaining their graduate recruitment, albeit with a reduced number of openings compared with the bumper recruitment levels seen two or three years ago.

There are also literally thousands of small and medium-sized businesses that rely on hiring ambitious new graduates for their organisations, often recruiting direct from local universities. A poll of careers services at twenty-six leading UK universities in July 2009, conducted by High Fliers Research, revealed that they were promoting a combined total of more than 3,200 different organisations that were looking to take on new graduates – together offering at least 10,000 vacancies for university-leavers.

Given that there continues to be such a wide choice of different types of employment and graduate jobs, how then can prospective employers be assessed and ranked?

To find out, we interviewed over 16,000 final year students who graduated from universities across the UK in the summer of 2009, and asked them, "Which employer do you think offers the best opportunities for graduates?". Between them, the 'Class of 2009' named organisations in every imaginable employment sector – from the country's best-known retailers to the 'Big Four' accounting & professional services firms, government departments to charities, high street banks to consulting firms and leading IT companies. The one hundred employers who were mentioned most often during the research form *The Times Top 100 Graduate Employers*.

This book is therefore a celebration of the employers who are judged to offer the brightest prospects for graduates. Whether by the perceived quality of their training programmes, the business success that they enjoy, the scale of their organisations, or by the impression that their recruitment promotions have made – these are the employers that are most attractive to university-leavers in 2009.

The Times Top 100 Graduate Employers will not necessarily identify which organisation is right for you: only you can decide that. But it is an invaluable reference if you want to discover what Britain's leading employers have to offer new graduates.

Leaving university and finding your first job can be a daunting process but it is one of the most important steps you'll ever take. Having a good understanding of the range of opportunities available must be the best way to start.

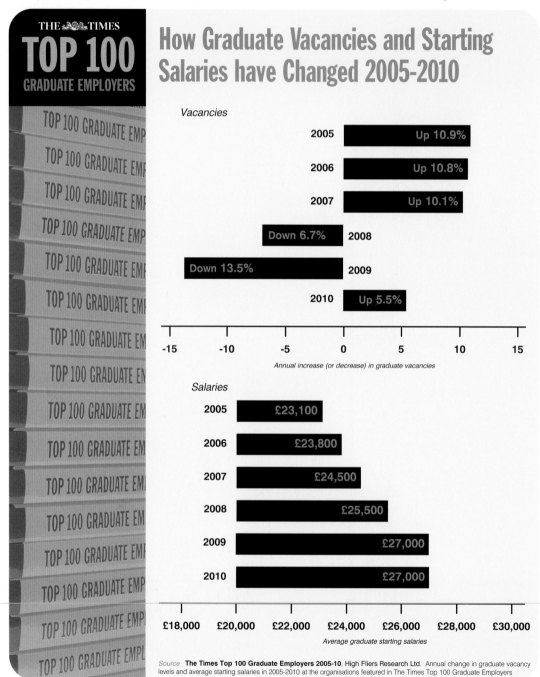

How Graduate Vacancies and Starting Salaries have Changed 2005-2010

Source **The Times Top 100 Graduate Employers 2005-10**, High Fliers Research Ltd. Annual change in graduate vacancy levels and average starting salaries in 2005-2010 at the organisations featured in The Times Top 100 Graduate Employers

Graduate recruitment down 47%

Aldi graduate recruitment up 50%

Aldi, one of the world's largest privately-owned companies, have recently announced that their award-winning grad~~uat~~ ~~re~~a m~~ana~~ge~~m~~ ~~t~~n tra~~in~~

Are you just going to make up the numbers?
Or really make the headlines?

First, the good news: Aldi are still looking to find the best and brightest to join their Graduate Area Management Training Programme. So, even though the papers may be full of doom and gloom, there's no reason for this year's high-fliers, go-getters or self-starters to worry. If you can stand out from the crowd, you can still look forward to a career in retailing that we guarantee will progress further – faster. You'll enjoy levels of responsibility unheard of in other companies. In fact, you won't just be your own boss – if all goes to plan, you'll be the boss of four to six Aldi stores within a few months.

No wonder our graduate programme gets such good press. Find out more on page 58 or online at **www.aldirecruitment.co.uk**

Graduate
Area Manager
£40,000
rising to
£60,000
after three years
Fully expensed
Audi A4
Opportunity
for directorship
within 5 years
International
secondment
opportunities

No bull.

Straight talking from KPMG.

Graduate Programmes – All degree disciplines

The truth is, we've got it all here at KPMG. The training and development you want. The level of support you need. And the type of professional, friendly environment you always hoped you'd end up working in.

For more straight talking, visit
www.kpmg.co.uk/careers

AUDIT ■ TAX ■ ADVISORY

KPMG

Compiling the Top 100 Graduate Employers

by Gill Thomas
Publisher, High Fliers Publications Ltd

The recession may have taken its toll on graduate recruitment, with fewer entry-level vacancies for university leavers at Britain's best-known employers, but there are still an estimated five thousand organisations who are expecting to hire graduates from UK universities during the 2009-2010 recruitment season.

Such a wide choice of employment can make selecting the organisation that is 'right' for you quite a challenge. How should you evaluate the different opportunities and what determines which employers offer the best graduate positions? What criteria can you use to assess so many different organisations and jobs?

There are no simple answers to these questions and clearly no single individual employer can ever hope to be right for every graduate. Everyone makes their own judgement about the organisations they want to work for and the type of job they find the most attractive.

So how can anyone produce a meaningful league table of Britain's leading graduate employers? What criteria can define whether one organisation is 'better' than another? To compile *The Times Top 100 Graduate Employers*, the independent market research company, High Fliers Research, interviewed 16,357 final year students who left UK universities in the summer of 2009.

These students from the 'Class of 2009' who took part in the study were selected at random to represent the full cross-section of finalists at their universities, not just those who had already secured graduate employment. The research examined students' experiences during their search for a graduate job and asked them about their attitudes to employers.

The key question used to produce the *Top 100* was, "Which employer do you think offers the best opportunities for graduates?" This question was deliberately open-ended and students were not prompted in any way. Across the whole survey, finalists mentioned more than 900 different organisations – from the smallest local employers, to some of the world's best-known companies. The responses were analysed to identify the number of times each employer was mentioned. The one hundred organisations that were mentioned most often are the *The Times Top 100 Graduate Employers* for 2009.

It is clear from the considerable selection of answers given by finalists from the 'Class of 2009' that individual students used very different criteria to determine which employer they considered offered the best opportunities for graduates. Some focused on employers' general reputations – their public image, their business profile or their commercial success. Others evaluated employers based on the information they had seen during their job search – the quality of recruitment promotions, the impression formed from meeting employers' representatives, or

THE ⚜ TIMES

TOP 100

GRADUATE EMPLOYERS

The Top 100 Graduate Employers 2009

This Year	Last Year		This Year	Last Year	
1.	1	PricewaterhouseCoopers	51.	21	Morgan Stanley
2.	2	Deloitte	52.	46	WPP
3.	8	Aldi	53.	51	Barclays Capital
4.	6	Civil Service	54.	63	Freshfields Bruckhaus Deringer
5.	3	KPMG	55.	58	ExxonMobil
6.	5	NHS	56.	66	GCHQ
7.	4	Accenture	57.	67	Arcadia Group
8.	9	Teach First	58.	76	Sky
9.	7	BBC	59.	35	UBS
10.	11	Ernst & Young	60.	93	MI5 – The Security Service
11.	15	Army	61.	73	Lovells
12.	16	Shell	62.	61	The Co-operative Group
13.	13	Procter & Gamble	63.	72	DLA Piper
14.	12	HSBC	64.	68	Herbert Smith
15.	14	GlaxoSmithKline	65.	74	McDonald's Restaurants
16.	19	BP	66.	94	Ministry of Defence
17.	20	Tesco	67.	65	British Airways
18.	23	IBM	68.	NEW	BDO Stoy Hayward
19.	10	Goldman Sachs	69.	55	HBOS
20.	24	Google	70.	62	Oxfam
21.	25	Rolls-Royce	71.	89	Transport for London
22.	31	Microsoft	72.	NEW	nucleargraduates
23.	27	L'Oréal	73.	41	Bank of America Merrill Lynch
24.	22	J.P. Morgan	74.	59	Bain & Company
25.	37	BT	75.	60	Boots
26.	26	Clifford Chance	76.	NEW	Network Rail
27.	28	Police	77.	86	Airbus
28.	17	Marks & Spencer	78.	53	Bloomberg
29.	49	Local Government	79.	84	Penguin
30.	29	Allen & Overy	80.	71	Boston Consulting Group
31.	39	Mars	81.	81	E.ON
32.	33	Unilever	82.	82	Asda
33.	18	Royal Bank of Scotland Group	83.	88	Corus
34.	44	Arup	84.	90	QinetiQ
35.	32	Barclays Bank	85.	96	npower
36.	36	BAE Systems	86.	NEW	Dstl
37.	69	Atkins	87.	NEW	Apple
38.	48	McKinsey & Company	88.	43	AstraZeneca
39.	54	Lloyds TSB	89.	NEW	Lidl
40.	45	Foreign Office	90.	78	Innocent Drinks
41.	57	Slaughter and May	91.	NEW	EDF Energy
42.	40	Linklaters	92.	NEW	HP
43.	38	Deutsche Bank	93.	NEW	Nestlé
44.	42	RAF	94.	70	Credit Suisse
45.	47	John Lewis Partnership	95.	NEW	Environment Agency
46.	34	Cancer Research UK	96.	98	Metaswitch Networks (formerly Data Connection)
47.	95	Cadbury	97.	NEW	Financial Services Authority
48.	30	Citi	98.	NEW	Norton Rose
49.	50	Sainsbury's	99.	97	Grant Thornton
50.	52	Royal Navy	100.	NEW	Siemens

Source **The UK Graduate Careers Survey 2009**, High Fliers Research Ltd. 16,357 final year students leaving UK universities in the summer of 2009 were asked 'Which employer do you think offers the best opportunities for graduates?'

experiences through the recruitment and selection process. Finalists also considered the level of vacancies that organisations were recruiting for as an indicator of possible employment prospects, or were influenced by employers' profile on campus.

Many final year students, however, used the 'employment proposition' as their main guide – the quality of graduate training and development an employer offers, the salary & remuneration package available, and the practical aspects of a first job such as location or working hours.

Regardless of the criteria that students used to arrive at their answer, the hardest part for many was just selecting a single organisation. To some extent, choosing two or three, or even half a dozen employers would have been much easier. But the whole purpose of the exercise was to replicate the reality that everyone faces – you can only work for one organisation. And at each stage of the job search there are choices to be made as to which direction to take and which employers to pursue.

The resulting *Top 100* is a dynamic league table of the UK's most exciting and well-respected graduate recruiters in 2009. For a sixth consecutive year, PricewaterhouseCoopers – the accounting and professional services firm – has been voted the UK's leading graduate employer with a total of 8.0 per cent of finalists' votes. After winning the top spot in 2008 by the narrowest of margins, this year PwC's lead over arch rivals Deloitte is a more convincing margin of two hundred votes. This is the fourth year running that Deloitte has been ranked in second place.

The seemingly unstoppable retailer Aldi has more than doubled its vote this year and jumped five places, joining the top three for the first time. It is just seven years since the company appeared in *The Times Top 100 Graduate Employers* as a new entry in 65th place and it has risen each year since. The Civil Service has also seen a sharp increase in its votes this year and has moved up to 4th place.

Despite polling slightly more votes than in 2008, both KPMG and the NHS slip down the rankings to 5th and 6th places respectively. Accenture, the consulting and technology company, has dropped three places to 7th and the BBC is down to 9th place this year, its lowest

ranking since 2002. The widely acclaimed Teach First scheme has climbed another place to 8th position, its sixth consecutive rise up the rankings since entering the *Top 100* in 63rd place in 2003. Ernst & Young move up one place to reach the top ten for the first time.

The Army has moved back up the rankings for the second year running and is now in 11th place. Oil giants Shell and BP have both improved their positions and are in 12th and 16th places respectively. Britain's most-successful retailer, Tesco, has climbed a further three places this year to 17th, IBM has returned to the top twenty for the first time since 2006 and Google is up four places to 20th position.

The City's disastrous year in the wake of the 'credit crunch', the collapse of Lehman Brothers and the resulting global financial meltdown has had a very dramatic impact on the rankings of banks and financial institutions in the *Top 100*. Goldman Sachs has seen its vote halved this year, dropping to 19th place, the RBS Group has crashed out of the top thirty and UBS, Credit Suisse and Morgan Stanley have each fallen more than twenty places in the rankings. The only bank that managed to go up in this year's *Top 100* is Lloyds TSB – now a part of the enlarged Lloyds Banking Group – which has climbed fifteen to 39th place.

The highest climbers in 2009 are led by Cadbury which has leapt an impressive forty-eight places to 47th, MI5 - The Security Service which moves up thirty-three places to 60th place, and Atkins which jumps thirty-two places to 37th in the *Top 100*. The Ministry of Defence – best known for its graduate engineering & science programme – also did well, climbing from 94th up to 66th position.

There are thirteen new entries in this year's *Top 100*, the highest being BDO Stoy Hayward, the accounting and professional services firm. nucleargraduates – an innovative new scheme launched by the Nuclear Decommissioning Authority to recruit graduates to work in more than twenty employers across the UK's nuclear industry – appears in 72nd place, just ahead of Network Rail. Apple, the popular computer and iPod maker, joins the rankings for the first time in 87th place and discount retailer Lidl and energy group EDF Energy appear in 89th and 91st places respectively.

Seven organisations – Dstl, HP, Nestlé, the Environment Agency, the Financial Services Authority, Norton Rose and Siemens – have each returned to the *Top 100* after dropping out of the list in previous years.

Organisations leaving the *Top 100* in 2009 include the investment bank Lehman Brothers, the Bank of America, BNP Paribas, law firms Addleshaw Goddard, Eversheds and CMS Cameron McKenna, consulting firms Oliver Wyman and Watson Wyatt, Pfizer, Faber Maunsell, Fujitsu, Thomson Reuters and the Met Office.

This year's edition of *The Times Top 100 Graduate Employers* has produced a number of significant changes, particularly towards the top of the list, and the results provide a unique insight into how graduates from the 'Class of 2009' rated the leading employers. The majority of these organisations are featured in the 'Employer Entry' section of this book. Starting on page 51, you can see a two-page profile for each employer, listed alphabetically for easy reference.

The editorial part of the entry includes a short description of what the organisation does, its opportunities for graduates and its recruitment programme for 2009-2010. A fact file for each employer gives details of the number of graduate vacancies, the business functions that graduates are recruited for, likely starting salaries for 2010, application deadlines, the universities that the employer is intending to visit during the year, and contact details for their recruitment website and graduate brochure. The right-hand page of the entry contains a display advert from the employer.

If you would like to find out more about any of the employers featured in *The Times Top 100 Graduate Employers*, then you can use the book's 'Information Request Service' – simply register your personal details and the employers you are interested in using the request card that appears opposite page 224, or go online to **www.Top100GraduateEmployers.com** – the official website showcasing the latest news and information about *Top 100* organisations.

You'll receive email bulletins about the employers, details of their presentations and careers events at your university, and other information about their graduate recruitment. The service is entirely free and you choose which organisations you would like to hear about.

Using the 'Information Request Service' enters you into a prize draw to win **£5,000**. There are also one hundred **£50 iTunes vouchers** to be won – two at each of the universities at which *The Times Top 100 Graduate Employers* book is distributed – for those who return information request cards before **30th November 2009**.

THE TIMES TOP 100 GRADUATE EMPLOYERS

Employers in this year's Top 100

#	Employer	Number of Employers
1.	Public Sector Employer	15
2.	Retailer	11
3.	Investment Bank	9
4.	Law Firm	9
5.	Engineering or Industrial Company	9
6.	IT or Telecoms Company	7
7.	Fast-Moving Consumer Goods Company	7
8.	Oil or Energy Company	6
9.	Accountancy or Professional Services Firm	6
10.	Bank or Financial Institution	5
11.	Consulting Firm	4
12.	Media Company	4
13.	Armed Forces	3
14.	Chemical or Pharmaceutical Company	2
15.	Charity or Voluntary Sector	2
16.	Other	1

Source **The UK Graduate Careers Survey 2009**, High Fliers Research Ltd. 16,357 final year students leaving UK universities in the summer 2009 were asked 'Which employer do you think offers the best opportunities for graduates?'

1NDIVIDUAL?

Assurance
Tax
Financial Advisory
Actuarial
Consulting
PwC Legal

Nationwide Opportunities Spring and Autumn 2010

It's our range of viewpoints that helps us answer the big business questions. That's why your degree discipline is far less important than the courage to speak up and the confidence to express your opinions. Bright, self-assured people make us the best at what we do. A firm that, for the sixth year running, is proud to be voted number one in the Times Top 100 Graduate Employers survey. So if you can think for yourself, shouldn't you be thinking for us?

Requirements:
2:1 in any degree discipline.
From 300 UCAS tariff or equivalent.

pwc.com/uk/careers/

Text: PwC to 85792 to visit our website on your mobile
(Texts charged at your standard network rate).

We value diversity in our people.

PRICEWATERHOUSE COOPERS

The Times Graduate Recruitment Awards

As well as *The Times Top 100 Graduate Employers* league table, students from the 'Class of 2009' were also asked 'Which employer would you most like to work for?' to identify the 'graduate employers of choice' for different career destinations. The winners of *The Times Graduate Recruitment Awards 2009* are listed here:

Source **The UK Graduate Careers Survey 2009**, High Fliers Research Ltd. 16,357 final year students leaving university in the summer 2009 were asked 'Which employer do you most want to work for?' within the career sectors they had applied to.

How to use the directory

Many of the employers listed within The Times Top 100 Graduate Employers are featured in the 'Employer Entries' section of the directory. These entries describe what each organisation does, the opportunities they offer graduates, and practical details about their recruitment programme for 2009-2010.

The 'Employer Entry' section begins on page 51.

Each entry follows a standard format, and contains two elements: descriptive text and easy-to-find information on the employer's vacancies, contact details and salary expectations.

Locations of jobs
The regional locations of the employer's jobs are highlighted in red.

Vacancies
The number of likely graduate vacancies at this employer in 2009-2010

Career areas recruited for
Details of the generic career areas that the employer recruits into. There are 17 areas to look out for:

- Accountancy
- Consulting
- Engineering
- Finance
- General Management
- Human Resources
- Investment Banking
- IT
- Law
- Logistics
- Manufacturing
- Marketing
- Media
- Purchasing
- Research & Development
- Retailing
- Sales

Employer's graduate recruitment website

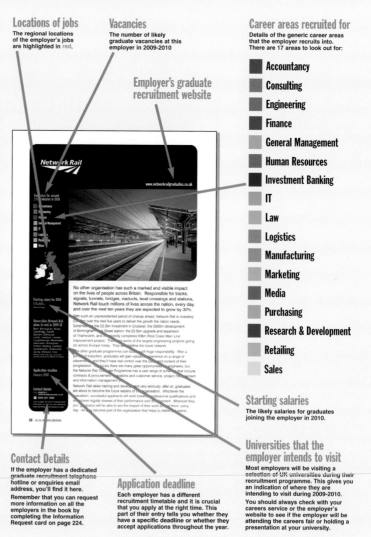

Starting salaries
The likely salaries for graduates joining the employer in 2010.

Universities that the employer intends to visit
Most employers will be visiting a selection of UK universities during their recruitment programme. This gives you an indication of where they are intending to visit during 2009-2010. You should always check with your careers service or the employer's website to see if the employer will be attending the careers fair or holding a presentation at your university.

Contact Details
If the employer has a dedicated graduate recruitment telephone hotline or enquiries email address, you'll find it here. Remember that you can request more information on all the employers in the book by completing the Information Request card on page 224.

Application deadline
Each employer has a different recruitment timetable and it is crucial that you apply at the right time. This part of their entry tells you whether they have a specific deadline or whether they accept applications throughout the year.

At npower we are driven by one overriding desire... to be the very best. That's why we're looking for graduates with the same desire and the opportunity to fulfil it.

Energy generation and supply offers one of the most dynamic career paths for graduates who can bring inspiration to the way we work. If you have the enthusiasm, commitment and the capacity to learn we'll give you the chance to shine. Our graduate programme will expose you to all the facets of our business and quickly give you responsibility within your chosen area.

If this sounds like the challenge you're looking for visit our website today.

THE TIMES
TOP 50
WHERE WOMEN WANT TO WORK
2008

visit www.brightergraduates.com

Power. Innovation

Graduate opportunities

As one of the best known and most respected names in engineering, we have built success on a century's worth of excellence and innovation. But with £56bn worth of orders on our books, an annual R&D spend of £900m, and a fir commitment to recruit more graduates than we've ever do before, we firmly believe our best years are ahead of us.

Progress.

R, Manufacturing Leadership, Project Management, Purchasing, Supply Chain

ve your career some forward momentum. Join a global
usiness providing power systems for use on land, at sea & in
e air. Visit www.rolls-royce.com/university

Trusted to deliver excellence

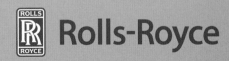

There are still 0,000 reasons for graduates to get out of bed

Job hopes plunge (and debts rise) for graduates

ONLY a third of graduates expect to find a job after leaving univer-

Business warned graduate time bo...

Graduate recruitment by top employers falls to 2005 levels

acancies are still ou
sity careers servic

e news for graduates leav-
g university this summer
been unrelentingly
omy: a depressing combi
ior of record n

The only sectors that had
creased their graduate

and c
recrui
new
Ste
mem
of H
Cha

riet Ale

Students learn it's easier to get a degree than a j...

Danna Sugden

ens of thousands of students graduating
is year will have to join the dole queue,
according to research that paints a grim

the company says. Its predictions come
as other figures showed that gra
debt has almost reached £26 billior
pared with £18 billion in 2007.
Martin Birchall, the managing
of High Fliers, said that the
000 vacancies f
ma

of the 1994 Group of
universities, said that u
be allowed to make dif
rive up competition be
that think

Class of 2009 facing the worst job market 'in two decades'

Two-thirds of graduates don't expect to find good job

TIM ROSS

GRADUATE job offers have fallen by a
third as students face working in bars
or supermarkets after leaving university this summer, research showed
today.

Two thirds of graduates
to find a graduate-level
have completed their de
found. And as the reces
ment, students are turr
careers in banking in th
ing more secure work a
The annual survey of
dence in the
noted f

Graduate jo vanishing, s poll of recrui

olly Curtis
ducation editor

igures show 28% fewer
uate vacancies than in
tember last year

chard Garner
TION EDITOR

NUMBER of graduate jobs on
the Class of 2009 has been cut
r cent, according to figu
oday.
utbacks
tes f

now either filled their places, or have
closed off their applications process."
The report concludes: "The end-of-
year picture for recruitment... reveals
stantially during the 2009 recruitment
season and 13.5 per cent fewer gradu
ates will start work with the UK
ing companies
Thi

Graduates hit as job vacanc in City fall 6

Graduates struggle as employers cut posts

By Graeme Paton
Education Editor

UNIVERSITY leavers are
fa jobs crisis as leading
promising to guara

to fall by almost half. Th
conclusions, in an annu
survey by the marketing
High Fliers Research.
at a time that minist

Firms cut number of graduate jobs

The number of students
finding jobs during

Andrew Taylor,
loyment Correspondent

Hiring levels
tion of what th
ple of year
Thesiger con
vacancies

Worst job market for graduates in a decade as the recession bit

Carol Lewis

Only one in five final-year university
students expects to have secured a job
by time they graduate this summer.

The recession, high debts and
increasing numbers of students have
combined to create the toughest
graduate jobs market for a decade.

Figures based on face-to-face interviews with 16,357 final-year students
show that only 5 per cent had a defi-
nite job offer in March this year, com-
with 20 per cent last year.

rate graduate programmes have made
job offers by the new year. Nonethe-
less, 36 per cent of final-year students
expect to find a job this year — with
21 per cent expecting to have secured
one by the time they graduate.

Martin Birchall, managing director
of High Fliers Research, who conducted the survey, said: "Students
have reacted very quickly to the recession and there is a whole new mood of
realism in terms of the type of careers
many students are choosing. They
haven't applied to banking or consulting or City positions and instead they

have been focusing on areas like teaching, the public sector, the Armed
Forces — areas that are perceived to
have better job security and have a
more plentiful supply of vacancies."

Applications for jobs at investment
banks have fallen by 31 per cent this
year compared with last, accountancy
by 11 per cent, general finance by 9 per
cent and consulting by 9 per cent.

The drop in applications to investment banks coincides with a 38 per
cent fall in vacancies, but competition
remains stiff: in the boom years
investment banks received 100 to 150

applications for each vacancy; now it
is likely to be nearer to 30 to 50.

The most popular sectors among
student job-hunters are teaching, the
media and marketing — despite a
dearth of jobs in the latter two. If the
survey results are extrapolated to all
universities, there will be some 4,200
applicants for every media, pr and
advertising graduate job this year.

Graduates have curbed earning
hopes, expecting on average to start
on £22,300 — £500 less than last year.
Chris Pateman, 21, an English Litera-
ture student at Exeter University, has

applied for a nu
and marketing jol
an interview". He
paid work experie
agency before w
abroad. He will
advertising roles
consider other ro

Despite the st
Lammy, the
Minister, said: "I
and a rewarding
degree remains e
achieve it."

Recession

Understanding the Graduate Market

by Martin Birchall
Managing Director, High Fliers Research

It's now more than two years since the 'credit crunch' took hold, throwing the global banking system into crisis – stock markets crashed, house prices tumbled, unemployment soared, the UK slumped into recession and four years of growth in the graduate job market came to an abrupt end.

For graduates leaving university in 2009, the newspaper headlines spelt out the bleak news – there were significantly fewer vacancies at Britain's best-known employers and competition for the graduate jobs that remained reached unprecedented levels. The outlook, however, for the 'Class of 2010' is a little more encouraging – vacancies at *The Times Top 100 Graduate Employers* are set to increase by a modest 5.5 per cent in 2010. Whilst this is very welcome news, it only restores around a quarter of the vacancies lost during the previous two recruitment seasons. Together, the employers in this year's *Top 100* are advertising 15,884 jobs, compared to the 15,057 graduates hired in 2009.

The financial sector was one of the employment areas hardest hit at the start of the 'credit crunch' but it is amongst the first to show early signs of recovery. City investment banks expect to recruit a fifth more graduates in 2010, compared with the numbers hired in 2009, other banking and financial groups are set to increase their intake by 8 per cent and accountancy firms are offering 5 per cent more vacancies.

Other sectors are cautiously optimistic too. The leading engineering & industrial companies and consumer goods manufacturers are set to recruit around 10 per cent more graduates in the coming year and similar growth is expected at public sector employers too.

Vacancy numbers are unchanged in the oil and energy industry, for the Armed Forces and in consulting but there are expected to be a few less entry-level positions available in retail and at the top law firms in 2010. Recruitment for the IT and telecommunications sector faces the biggest cuts – almost 10 per cent fewer graduate vacancies than in 2009.

There are now an average of 160 vacancies per *Top 100* employer but one in eight organisations plan to hire at least 250 new recruits and two employers anticipate hiring at least 1,000 university-leavers in 2010.

In all, two-fifths of leading employers plan to hire more graduates this recruitment season than last, just under half believe they will recruit similar numbers to 2009, while a sixth expect to cut their total graduate intake.

The largest number of vacancies in 2010 are at accountancy firms (22.0 per cent of total graduate jobs) and the public sector employers (15.5 per cent of total). Together the 'Big Four' accountancy firms – Deloitte, Ernst & Young, KPMG and PricewaterhouseCoopers – plan to recruit more than 3,100 new graduates and the

HELP SHAPE THE FUTURE OF BANKING.

Graduate and Undergraduate opportunities

As the UK's largest financial services organisation, we aim to build our leadership position not on the basis of our size, but on the foundations of reputation and recommendation. We want you to help us achieve this.

To find out more about the opportunities available to you to help shape the future of banking, go to Page 152.

LLOYDS BANKING GROUP

 Lloyds TSB   HALIFAX   BANK OF SCOTLAND   C&G Cheltenham & Gloucester   BM BIRMINGHAM MIDSHIRES  SCOTTISH WIDOWS

public sector is particularly strong in this year's *Top 100*, with a record fifteen Government departments, agencies or other organisations appearing in the latest league table.

The employers who plan to hire the fewest graduates in 2009 are those in the chemical & pharmaceutical sector (0.4 per cent of total graduate jobs), consumer goods (1.2 per cent) and the charity & voluntary sector (1.3 per cent).

The biggest individual graduate recruiters in *The Times Top 100 Graduate Employers* during 2009-2010 are PricewaterhouseCoopers and Deloitte (1,000 vacancies each), the Army (900 vacancies), the newly-expanded Teach First

scheme (700 places), KPMG (650 vacancies), the RAF (600 vacancies) and Ernst & Young, the Royal Navy and Civil Service Fast Stream (each 500 vacancies). The smallest recruiters are WPP, the Environment Agency, Nestlé and Cadbury, which each plan to hire fewer than 20 graduates for their organisations in 2010.

Over half the employers featured in the *Top 100* have vacancies for graduates in financial management or IT, a third have opportunities in engineering and human resources, a quarter are looking for marketing or sales executives, a fifth have roles in purchasing and logistics, whilst one in six are looking for retail personnel.

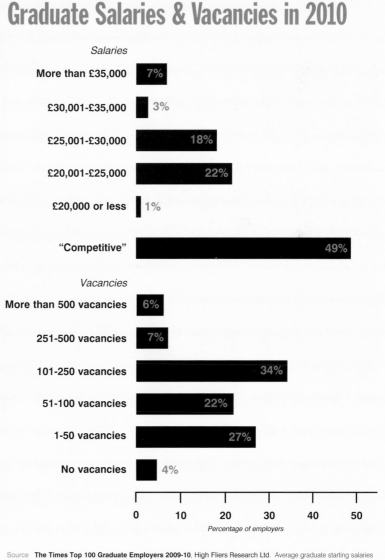

Graduate Salaries & Vacancies in 2010

Salaries

More than £35,000	7%
£30,001-£35,000	3%
£25,001-£30,000	18%
£20,001-£25,000	22%
£20,000 or less	1%
"Competitive"	49%

Vacancies

More than 500 vacancies	6%
251-500 vacancies	7%
101-250 vacancies	34%
51-100 vacancies	22%
1-50 vacancies	27%
No vacancies	4%

Percentage of employers

Source **The Times Top 100 Graduate Employers 2009-10**, High Fliers Research Ltd. Average graduate starting salaries and total number of graduate vacancies in 2010 at the organisations featured in The Times Top 100 Graduate Employers.

Recent results from *The UK Graduate Careers Survey 2009* – a survey of more than 16,000 final year students conducted by High Fliers Research – showed that almost half of new graduates wanted to work in London for their first job. It's good news then that more than three-quarters of *Top 100* employers have graduate vacancies in the capital and half have posts available elsewhere in the south east of England. Half also have vacancies in Yorkshire, the Midlands, the south west and north west of England and in Scotland. Fewer than two-fifths of organisations have opportunities in Wales or Northern Ireland. The region with the fewest graduate employers is East Anglia.

One consequence of the recession has been the freezing of graduate starting salaries at many well-known employers. More than three-quarters of the organisations in this year's edition of *The Times Top 100 Graduate Employers* have opted to leave their 2010 starting salaries unchanged from last year. Only a fifth of employers have increased their graduate packages this year, most by less than 5 per cent and two companies have reduced their starting salaries. The average pay for new graduates is £27,000, the same as in 2009 – the first time in more than a decade that there has been no annual rise in graduate pay.

Almost half of *Top 100* employers simply describe their packages as "competitive". Nearly

THE TIMES TOP 100 GRADUATE EMPLOYERS

Changes to Salaries & Vacancies in 2010

Salaries

More than a 5% salary rise	3%
Up to a 5% salary rise	12%
Up to a 2.5% salary rise	5%
No change from 2009	78%
A reduction in salary	2%

Vacancies

More than 50 extra vacancies	10%
26-50 extra vacancies	7%
1-25 extra vacancies	23%
No change from 2009	42%
1-25 fewer vacancies	9%
26-50 fewer vacancies	6%
More than 50 fewer vacancies	3%

0   20   40   60   80   100
Percentage of employers

Source **The Times Top 100 Graduate Employers 2009-10**, High Fliers Research Ltd. Graduate starting salaries & vacancy levels in 2010, compared with recruitment in 2009 at the organisations featured in The Times Top 100 Graduate Employers

How do you feel about your future?
You should feel nothing but excitement

Graduate Vacancies

Now that you're about to graduate, is life looking less certain? Your career prospects might seem daunting now, but your knuckles needn't go white over every possible future twist or turn. We'll help you choose the right professional services role – Tax, Audit, Corporate Finance or Consulting – and guide you towards your professional qualifications. If you need study leave or assistance with managing your workload, you'll have it. On joining us, you'll also have a personal mentor – someone who can appraise and encourage you as you progress. In short, we'll put you on the right track to success. Staying there, however, is down to you. It's your future. How far will you take it?

official professional services provider
to the Olympic and Paralympic Games

Deloitte.

Discover more at
www.deloitte.co.uk/graduates

a quarter pay new graduates up to £25,000 and seven organisations – typically either investment banks or City law firms – offer starting salaries in excess of £35,000. But the most generous graduate package on offer in 2010 is Aldi's – they're providing their new recruits with a starting salary of £40,000 as well as a fully-expensed Audi A4 company car. None of the *Top 100* employers which publish starting salary details are paying less than £20,000 to their new graduates this year.

The majority of the organisations listed in *The Times Top 100 Employers* are actively marketing their graduate vacancies at between 15 and 20 UK universities this year. Recruiters use a variety of careers fairs, campus presentations, local advertising and promotions with the university careers services. The universities likely to host the most events run by Britain's top graduate employers in 2009-2010 are Manchester, London, Warwick, Cambridge, Oxford, Nottingham, Bath, Bristol and Leeds.

Half of the UK's leading employers now recruit all the year-round and will accept applications throughout the 2009-2010 recruitment season, until all their vacancies have been filled. For employers with a single application deadline, the majority are in either November or December, although most law firms usually have July closing dates.

There are lots of reasons to feel positive about life after graduation. Despite the drop in graduate vacancies over the last two years, the number of positions for university-leavers at *Top 100* employers is still 15 per cent higher than in 2004 and starting salaries for new graduates have increased by around a fifth over the same period.

Few people can expect to walk straight into a job – there is tough competition for all vacancies and the UK's top employers have rigorous selection procedures which include online applications, initial interviews, aptitude tests and final-round assessment centres. Graduates not only need to gain a good degree – most of the top employers want to recruit those with a first or 2.1 – but also develop key skills along the way. Employers look for well-rounded individuals with demonstrable competencies such as the ability to work well in teams, motivation and organisation, communication skills and leadership potential.

But for those finalists who do make the grade, there continue to be many rewarding careers and some great starting salaries on offer at *The Times Top 100 Graduate Employers*.

THE ☙ TIMES
TOP 100
GRADUATE EMPLOYERS

Graduate Employment in 2010, by Industry

	2009		% of total vacancies in 2010	How graduate vacancies compare with 2009
1.	1	Accountancy or Professional Services Firms	22.0	Up 5.2%
2.	3	Public Sector	15.5	Up 9.0%
3.	4	Armed Forces	12.6	No change
4.	2	Investment Banks or Fund Managers	12.0	Up 18.9%
5.	6	Banking or Financial Services	7.2	Up 7.7%
6.	7	Retailers	6.4	Down 1.1%
7.	5	Engineering or Industrial Companies	6.3	Up 9.4%
8.	8	Law Firms	5.3	Down 3.7%
9.	11	Oil & Energy Companies	3.1	No change
10.	9	Consulting Firms	2.5	No change
11.	10	IT & Telecommunications Companies	2.1	Down 9.8%
12.	12	Media Organisations	2.0	Up 6.9%
13.	13	Charity or Voluntary Organisations	1.3	Up 17.6%
14.	14	Consumer Goods Manufacturers	1.2	Up 10.7%
15.	15	Chemical & Pharmaceuticals	0.4	Up 18.2%

Source **The Times Top 100 Graduate Employers 2009-10**, High Fliers Research Ltd. Graduate vacancy levels in 2010, compared with total numbers recruited in 2009 at the organisations featured in The Times Top 100 Graduate Employers

BETH
LOMAX
BATH

ROSHAN
NILAWEERA
BRISTOL

LAURA
HOUSE
CAMBRIDGE

BEN
BARTLETT
EDINBURGH

Join in, stand out.

you could really make a difference, would you?
you could change children's lives, would you?
you could inspire and lead them to achieve their potential, would you?

d if doing all this changed your own future too, the real question is why wouldn't you?

Teach First

LEARNING TO LEAD

www.teachfirst.org.uk

istered charity no: 1098294

Star quality?

Graduate Management Programme
LOCATIONS NATIONWIDE

Can you deliver star qualities? If you can lead and inspire as part of a team, take the next step now towards applying to work for a world-class retailer.

Our graduate management programme is for outstanding, self-confident individuals, who can make a significant difference to our business from day one.

For more information on how to apply, please visit **www.lidl.co.uk**

www.lidl.co.uk

Successful Job Hunting

by Jonathan Black
Director, University of Oxford Careers Service

Planning for the future and finding your first graduate job can seem a daunting process but it is one of the most important things that you'll do at university. Each year, at least a third of undergraduates say 'I don't know where to start' and a quarter worry that they don't have the skills needed to cope with the graduate recruitment process. Even those who have a clearer idea about what they want to do after graduation still need access to the latest job vacancy information.

Whatever stage you are at in your job search, help is available from your university careers service. Every university in the UK has its own careers or employment service, providing personal guidance, advice and support for students, as well as a wide range of information about different occupations, individual employers and graduate vacancies.

There's no 'right time' to begin using your university careers service. Some people want to get started on their job search almost as soon as they arrive at university, others wait until they're looking for work experience or vacation work in their second year and many leave things until their final year of studies.

What you've studied at university may provide little clue to your future career. You could have done modern languages and end up doing strategic planning for the NHS – that's the beauty of the degree system. The key to making the right choice is doing your research – you need to talk to your friends, to your parents and family, to academic staff and to employers to really understand the possibilities and what you may be suited to. At some point, you may also value talking to a university careers adviser who are very experienced in helping students at all stages of their career search.

In many ways, a careers adviser is like a mentor. They're not going to say 'you should do this job' nor will they give you specific contacts with employers, but they can guide you through the job hunting process, challenge your thinking and prompt you to consider other options.

It's all about knowing yourself and what you really enjoy doing – and being totally honest about it. If you enjoy working with children or hate being in an office, then there's little point thinking about banking. Draw on your own experiences so far to help you – if you enjoyed being in the cadets at school or like being outdoors or thrive on solving problems or did well at physics, all of these are clues about what you might like to do in the future.

Few people have one career anymore – you're much more likely to do lots of separate things, so what you do straightaway is not going to bind you in for life. Even within vocations such as medicine and engineering, you can move off into other things, so it's not forever. What's important is to think about what you are going to do first

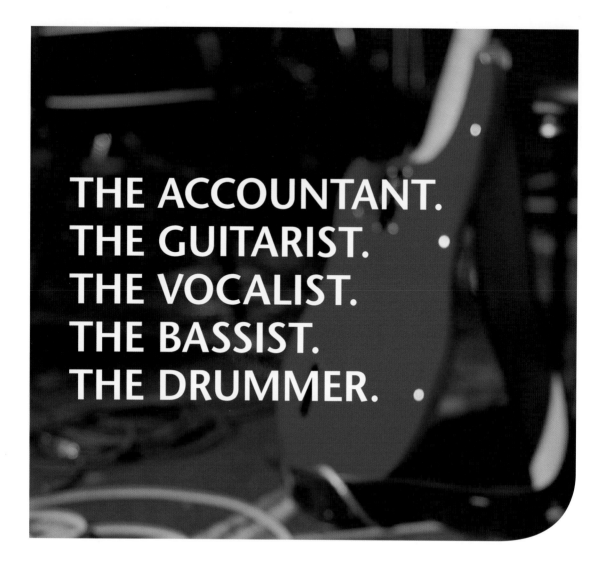

THE ACCOUNTANT.
THE GUITARIST.
THE VOCALIST.
THE BASSIST.
THE DRUMMER.

Essential for keeping the show on the road

There are a multitude of career opportunities for graduates, but how can you be sure that you've got what it takes to secure your dream position? The ACA qualification from the ICAEW will give you access to a variety of career opportunities from working in accountancy practice, to industry, or the public sector. Every business needs an ACA qualified chartered accountant, so visit our website and found out how you can strike a chord in the business world.

To find out more:
E careers@icaew.com
www.icaew.com/careers

THE INSTITUTE
OF CHARTERED
ACCOUNTANTS
IN ENGLAND AND WALES

and especially what that might lead to.

There are a number of web-based tools that you can use to help you with your decision-making process – such as Prospects Planner, an online job exploration which is available on the Prospects website, and the HBDI brain dominance system that helps you identify your preferred thinking style; for example, if you prefer working with detail, then you're unlikely to enjoy strategic planning or creative marketing roles. If it's the other way round, then you're not really going to enjoy being an accountant. Most careers services also have an excellent supply of occupational briefings that help describe the opportunities in many different career destinations.

Personally, I think the best way to find out about different career areas is to talk to people. You can start by contacting recent alumni from your university – your careers service has a database of former students who you can speak to about their experiences – or speak to people on employers' stands at careers fairs. Many fairs are now based around particular industries like finance, consulting or engineering but all of these, as well as general fairs, can be a good way to learn about the breadth of opportunities available.

Nobody likes talking to strangers but it's something you need to get good at if you're going to find out the information you need. Once you've done it once or twice you'll realise it's not as hard as it seems. If you can, I'd try to go to at least one careers fair before your final year. It doesn't take much time – a couple of hours out of your afternoon – and it can really help you to understand the careers landscape.

An early trip to a careers fair might also help you secure some work experience – either for a summer vacation or for a couple of weeks at Christmas or Easter. It's a superb opportunity to discover whether you really want to do a particular kind of work as a graduate. Without any experience it'll be hard to know for sure what type of work you are suited to and you'll have less to talk about in recruitment interviews. Any experience – however short, and irrespective of whether it's paid or unpaid – can be included on your CV and boosts your chances of having your application taken seriously.

Employers' presentations can be another good way to find out about individual organisations. They fall into two groups – sales pitches and more interactive experiences. Employers themselves are becoming less enchanted with the straight sales presentations that just focus on what the organisation does and why you should work for them. Instead, more are opting for skills sessions or business games that show the kind of work that an organisation is involved in.

Having identified the kind of employer you might be interested in, the next stage is to prepare your CV. Help is available from your careers service either in group sessions and CV clinics or sometimes on a one-to-one basis with a careers adviser. Although most major employers have their own online application systems, I still think it's important to write your CV first – it forces you to think through 'what have I done, what have I achieved?'.

Putting together your CV shouldn't be difficult – the way to write them is to say 'what was I responsible for and what did I achieve?' for each part of your CV. Writing, "I ran the school chess club and we came second in the national championships" is exactly the sort of thing that should will help get you a job. Ultimately, recruiters want to know 'do you take responsibility?' and 'do you achieve things?' And having all the information about your achievements in one place is excellent preparation for completing employers' own application forms.

There is no magic number of applications that will guarantee you a job offer. If you make too many and don't research each application carefully, it will shine through at the pre-screening stage or at first interview that you're not really committed to their organisation. So firing off a couple of dozen applications and hoping for the best isn't going to work – each one you do make has to be researched seriously. You have to treat your applications like an essay or a piece of coursework – after all, it is the next few years of your life that is at stake. If that means working at one o'clock in the morning to get an application finished, then so be it.

If you've done an internship or had work experience with an organisation, you may already have a head start on other applicants. It's not uncommon for employers to remember 'that student who worked for us last summer and was really good' and then discover a few months later 'we've a new project starting – let's give them a ring and see what they're up to rather than going through a big recruitment exercise'.

Another important option is to try to build up your network of contacts. With up to fifty applicants chasing each graduate vacancy with the larger employers, the odds of landing a place aren't good.

One technique is to conduct 'information interviews' – speaking to alumni or other contacts to ask them about their work. Stress that you're not looking for a job, you simply want to find out more about what they do. Ask if you can come and meet them for ten or fifteen minutes. Treat it like an interview – turn up on time, dress smartly and have your questions ready.

The reason that information interviewing works so well is that it's a completely unthreatening process – you're not asking for something that they can't necessarily give you. Before you finish the meeting, ask for two more names of people they'd recommend you speak to. Write them a thank you note and you'll stand out as one in ten who does and they'll remember you. Who knows, three months later they might say 'let's not bother advertising, let's see if that graduate who came to see us is available'. It looks a time-consuming process but is great for building your confidence, gathering information and may turn out to be a direct route to employment.

If your applications are successful you will be invited to a first interview or possibly go straight to an assessment centre. Your careers service will almost certainly run group sessions for interview practice, something that will be invaluable, especially if you've not taken part in many interviews before. Sometimes employers will run mock-interviews at the careers service. Like most things, the more practice you do, the better you will become.

Assessment centres, in particular, can seem quite strange and you don't want your first one to be the final selection round for the job that you really want. Many careers services – and some major employers – run sessions on what it's like in assessment centres. Very few people are good at these experiences first time round, so you'll want to rehearse the different elements as much as you can before doing them for real.

Whereas your CV or application is the thing that gets you an interview, what gets you the job is your passion and careful preparation for the rest of the selection process. Employers are said to 'hire for attitude, train for skills', so you have to be able to demonstrate your passion for the role you've applied for and the industry that you want to enter. Graduate recruiters are likely to be most interested in all the things at the bottom of your CV – the outside interests, community activity – the things which show your true character and drive.

It's also essential that you know enough about the organisation itself – you don't need to quote the ins and outs of the balance sheet or who is on the board of directors, but you should have read their latest annual report and know which products they make or sell. I would also do an online news search to see what has come up recently about the organisation and others in the same industry. Don't just rely on their recruitment website or graduate brochure, you need to show you're better informed than that when they ask 'what issues is our company facing at the moment?'. Remember, interviews are a brilliant place to show off and you need to go to them with a few prepared messages which you'll weave into your answers and that show that you've done your homework.

One of the key questions you're bound to face is 'why do you want the job?' and your answer should be all about the company and not about you – explain what you can bring to the organisation, how you can take responsibility and achieve things for the company.

For those who do impress at interview and assessment centres, the final dilemma may be which job offer to accept. At this stage, your decision is a combination of gut feel – are you drawn to the organisation's culture and its people – and where the job might lead to in the future.

If you don't get the job offer that you're looking for, there are a number of other options. Further study might be a good alternative, provided you're not simply doing it to put off your job search – there's no guarantee that the economy is going to be any better when you graduate with your Masters, or that anyone cares that you've got a Masters. If you've studied an undergraduate degree in politics or history, for example, think very carefully about going on to do a Masters in the same subject – will the higher qualification really boost your CV when you apply to employers?

Choose. Connect. Grow.

Choose to work in an entrepreneurial culture where you will connect with high-profile clients and grow your career through valuable mentoring from senior financial services professionals. Whether your interest is in Global Markets, Investment Banking, Global Wealth & Investment Management, Research, Global Product Solutions, Risk Management, Technology, Human Resources or Card Services, our career opportunities are second to none.

bankofamerica.com/campusrecruiting

Bank of America
Merrill Lynch

A more vocational course might be a much smarter choice if you've already struggled to land a job in a competitive employment market.

Going traveling or volunteering can be a good option, especially for short periods, but you might do equally well by working with your friends on a start-up. And remember, not every employer wants to hire graduates to start in September – many smaller firms have opportunities at other times of the year which you'd need to apply for a few weeks before the starting date. Being out of the country won't help you land one of those jobs.

Whatever the outcome, please stay in touch with your university and its careers service. One day you'll be in work and could help the next generation of student job hunters find internships and work experience or become a mentor for an undergraduate. Or you yourself may want further careers guidance when you decide to move on from your first graduate job.

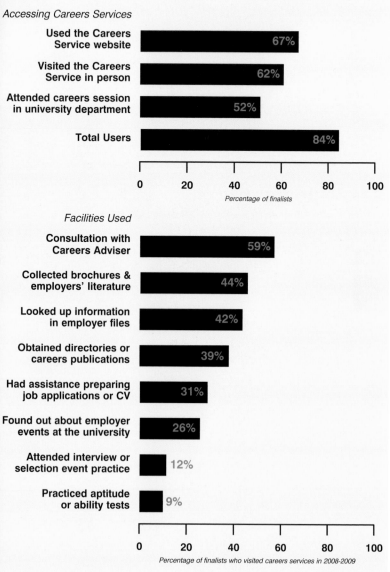

THE TIMES

TOP 100
GRADUATE EMPLOYERS

Usage of Careers Services in 2008-9

Accessing Careers Services

Used the Careers Service website	67%
Visited the Careers Service in person	62%
Attended careers session in university department	52%
Total Users	84%

0 20 40 60 80 100
Percentage of finalists

Facilities Used

Consultation with Careers Adviser	59%
Collected brochures & employers' literature	44%
Looked up information in employer files	42%
Obtained directories or careers publications	39%
Had assistance preparing job applications or CV	31%
Found out about employer events at the university	26%
Attended interview or selection event practice	12%
Practiced aptitude or ability tests	9%

0 20 40 60 80 100
Percentage of finalists who visited careers services in 2008-2009

Source **The UK Graduate Careers Survey 2009**, High Fliers Research Ltd. 16,357 final year students who left university in the summer of 2009 were asked about how they had used their local university careers service during 2008-2009.

Engineering.
Science.
Business.

500 places.
20+ companies.
One amazing scheme.

Please turn to page 184
to read our profile.

"Rated the #1 graduate recruitment website"

See for yourself why Milkround is first for graduate careers

The UK Graduate Careers Survey 2009 of 16,000 top university finalists found Milkround.com was the most widely-used commercial graduate recruitment website.

Visit Milkround.com for 100s of internships, placements, graduate schemes and jobs with The Times Top 100 Graduate Employers.

www.milkround.com

Milkround.com
FIRST FOR GRADUATE CAREERS

Top recruiters need top quality candidates
Target half a million high calibre students & graduates with
the UK's most popular graduate recruitment website

Find out more: 020 3003 4000 | sales@milkround.com | milkround.com/for-employers

THE TIMES
TOP 100 GRADUATE EMPLOYERS
TIMES
TOP 100 GRADUATE EMPLOYERS
2000-2001
TIMES
TOP 100 GRADUATE EMPLOYERS
2008-2009
THE TIMES
TOP 100 GRADUATE
TOP 100 GRADUATE EMPLOYERS
2001-2002
THE TIMES
TOP 100 GRADUATE EMPLOYERS
TIMES
TOP 100 GRADUATE EMPLOYERS
2004-2005

Ten Years of Researching Britain's Top Employers

by Gill Thomas
Publisher, The Times Top 100 Graduate Employers

In 1999, just as the first edition of *The Times Top 100 Graduate Employers* was being distributed at the UK's leading universities, Texas governor George W Bush announced he would run for the White House, eleven European countries were getting used to their new Euro currency, the world's computer industry was in turmoil at the prospect of the 'millennium bug' and Britney Spears' 'Baby One More Time' was the best-selling single of the year.

For new graduates fresh out of university, 1999 wasn't a bad time to be job hunting. Entry-level vacancies had shot up by more than 12 per cent the previous year, one of the largest annual increases since the late 1980s and starting salaries continued to rise at nearly twice the rate of inflation.

Final year students taking part in *The UK Graduate Careers Survey 1999* – the annual survey of finalists' career aspirations and expectations conducted by High Fliers Research – voted Andersen Consulting the year's top graduate employer and more finalists applied for jobs in management consulting than any other career area.

It is interesting to compare the results of that survey with the similar research carried out with the 'Class of 2009' earlier this year. In 1999 almost half of the top twenty employers that students thought offered the best opportunities for graduates were manufacturing or industrial companies. By contrast, just four of the organisations in this year's top twenty actually make anything – the list is dominated instead by accounting & professional services firms and public sector employers.

In 2009, typical salaries at a *Top 100* graduate employer are £27,000, more than 55% higher than the starting rates for graduates ten years ago. The average then was £17,400 and fewer than forty employers in the UK offered new recruits packages of £20,000 or more.

Only half of finalists used the internet in 1999 to research their career options but more than 40 per cent supported local university careers fairs. During the 2008-2009 recruitment season, although more than three-quarters of students relied on employers' websites as one of their primary sources of graduate job information, attendances at campus recruitment events remained as strong as ever.

Andersen Consulting is one of just three organisations that have made it to number one in *The Times Top 100 Graduate Employers* in the last ten years. The firm held on to the top spot for a further three years after 1999 and their success heralded a huge surge in popularity for careers in consulting. At its peak in 2001, almost one in six graduates applied for jobs in the sector.

In the year before the firm changed its name to Accenture, Andersen Consulting astutely introduced a new graduate package that

included a £28,500 starting salary (a sky-high figure for graduates in 2000) and a much talked-about £10,000 bonus, helping to assure the firm's popularity, irrespective of its corporate branding.

In 2003, after two dismal years in graduate recruitment when vacancies for university-leavers dropped by more than a fifth following the terrorist attacks of 11th September 2001, the Civil Service was named Britain's leading graduate employer. A year later it was displaced by PricewaterhouseCoopers, the accounting and professional services firm formed from the merger of Price Waterhouse and Coopers & Lybrand in 1998. At the time, the firm was the largest private-sector recruiter of graduates, hiring over 1,000 trainees annually.

PricewaterhouseCoopers has now stayed at number one for six years running, increasing its share of the student vote from 5 per cent in 2004 to more than 10 per cent in 2007. In 2008, the firm faced its stiffest competition yet from rivals Deloitte and retained the top ranking by just seven votes.

PwC's reign as the leading employer represents a remarkable renaissance for the entire accounting sector. Whereas a decade ago, a career in accountancy was widely regarded as a safe, traditional employment choice and the firms themselves were often derided as being 'dull', 'boring' or just 'bean-counters', today's profession is viewed in a very different light. The training required to become a chartered accountant is now seen as a prized business qualification and the sector's leading firms are regularly described as 'prestigious', 'dynamic' and 'international' by undergraduates looking for their first job after university.

Accountancy's transformation is underlined by the fact that fewer than 9 per cent of final year students opted for one of the top five accounting firms in the *Top 100* of 1999, compared with the 22 per cent of votes polled by the 'Big Four' firms in this year's list.

A total of 187 different organisations have now appeared within *The Times Top 100 Graduate Employers* since its inception. Just thirty-two of these have made it into the rankings every year since 1999. The most consistent performers over this period have been the Civil Service, KPMG and Accenture, each of which have never been lower than 8th place in the league table. Procter & Gamble has also had a formidable record, appearing in every top ten until 2005, and Ernst & Young, IBM and Unilever have each remained within the top quarter of the list throughout.

Arthur Andersen, the now defunct accounting firm, was actually the most consistently ranked employer in the history of the *Top 100*, achieving either 2nd or 3rd place every year between 1999 and the firm's demise in 2002. Pricewaterhouse-Coopers is the only other employer to have appeared within the top three in each of the years in which it has been listed in the *Top 100*.

Not all employers have been so successful. British Airways fell over eighty places in the years between 1999 and 2004 and high street chemist Boots has slumped from 10th in 1999 to 75th in this year's rankings. Ford, which was once rated

Movers & Shakers in the Top 100

Highest New Entries		Highest Climbing Employers	
1999	**Pfizer** (31st)	1999	**Schlumberger** (up 13 places)
2000	**Morgan Stanley** (34th)	2000	**Capital One** (up 32 places)
2001	**Marconi** (36th)	2001	**European Commission** (up 36 places)
2002	**Guinness UDV** (44th)	2002	**WPP** (up 36 places)
2003	**ASDA** (40th)	2003	**Rolls-Royce** (up 37 places)
2004	**Baker & McKenzie** (61st)	2004	**JPMorgan** (up 29 places)
2005	**Penguin** (70th)	2005	**Teach First** (up 22 places)
2006	**Fujitsu** (81st)	2006	**Google** (up 32 places)
2007	**BDO Stoy Hayward** (74th)	2007	**Pfizer** (up 30 places)
2008	**Sky** (76th)	2008	**Co-operative Group** (up 39 places)
2009	**BDO Stoy Hayward** (68th)	2009	**Cadbury** (up 48 places)

Source **The UK Graduate Careers Survey 1999-2009**, High Fliers Research Ltd, based on interviews with 162,776 students.

IT'S WHERE GRADUATES TURN

The Times is the No1 daily quality newspaper for graduates / students. *

THE TIMES

as high as 11th, fell out of the list in 2006 after cancelling its graduate recruitment two years previously.

Twenty-nine employers, including well-known names such as Nokia, Philips, the Home Office, Abbey, Coca Cola and British Sugar, have the dubious record of having only been ranked in the *Top 100* once during the decade, before disppearing without trace. Accounting firm BDO Stoy Hayward managed to be the highest new entry twice in both 2007 and 2009 but dropped out of the *Top 100* altogether in the intervening year. And Marconi had the unusual distinction of being one of the highest-ever new entries in 36th place in 2001, only to vanish from the list entirely the following year.

One of the most spectacular ascendancies within the *Top 100* has been the rise and rise of

Aldi which joined the list in 65th place in 2002 and is now ranked 3rd in 2009. Its eye-catching remuneration package (currently £40,000 plus an Audi A4 car for new graduates joining in 2009) coupled with the lofty job title of 'deputy area manager' for its new recruits and the promise of rapid career progression for those who thrive at the company, has really captured the imagination of increasing numbers of student job hunters.

And Teach First – the scheme which recruits graduates to work in the UK's most challenging schools for two years after university before they embark on careers in other areas – has been another runaway success in the rankings. After appearing in the *The Times Top 100 Graduate Employers* as a new entry in 63rd place in 2003, the scheme is currently ranked 8th and planning to recruit up to 500 graduates in 2010.

THE TIMES
TOP 100
GRADUATE EMPLOYERS

Winners & Losers in the Top 100

Most Consistent Employers 1999-2009

	Highest Ranking	Lowest Ranking
Arthur Andersen *	**2nd** (1999-2001)	**3rd** (2002)
PricewaterhouseCoopers *	**1st** (2004-2009)	**3rd** (1999-2001, 2003)
Civil Service	**1st** (2003)	**6th** (2008)
KPMG	**3rd** (2006-2008)	**8th** (1999)
Accenture (formerly Andersen Consulting)	**1st** (1999-2002)	**8th** (2006)
Ernst & Young	**10th** (2009)	**20th** (2001)
IBM	**13th** (2000)	**23rd** (2008)
Procter & Gamble	**3rd** (1998)	**15th** (2007)
Army	**4th** (2003)	**18th** (2007)
GlaxoSmithKline	**11th** (2000)	**26th** (1998)

* Employer did not feature in the Top 100 every year between 1999 and 2009

Employers Climbing Highest 1999-2009

	New Entry Ranking	Highest Ranking
Google	**85th** (2005)	**20th** (2009)
Aldi	**65th** (2002)	**3rd** (2009)
Teach First	**63rd** (2003)	**8th** (2009)
Oxfam	**95th** (2003)	**45th** (2006)
Cancer Research UK	**79th** (2004)	**34th** (2008)
Royal Bank of Scotland Group	**54th** (1999)	**15th** (2004-2006)
The Co-operative Group	**100th** (2007)	**61st** (2008)

Employers Falling Furthest 1999-2009

	Highest Ranking	Lowest Ranking
British Airways	**6th** (1999)	**87th** (2004)
Boots	**10th** (1999)	**75th** (2007, 2009)
Ford	**11th** (1999)	**Not ranked** (from 2006)
Ministry of Defence	**35th** (2003)	**Not ranked** (2007)
Marconi	**36th** (2001)	**Not ranked** (from 2002)
Logica	**39th** (1999)	**Not ranked** (from 2003)
Qinetiq	**43rd** (2001)	**Not ranked** (2007)

Source **The UK Graduate Careers Survey 1999-2009**, High Fliers Research Ltd, based on interviews with 162,776 students.

Top 10 Graduate Employers 1999-2008

1999
1. Andersen Consulting (now Accenture)
2. Arthur Andersen
3. PricewaterhouseCoopers
4. Procter & Gamble
5. Civil Service
6. British Airways
7. Marks & Spencer
8. KPMG
9. Unilever
10. Boots

2000
1. Andersen Consulting (now Accenture)
2. Arthur Andersen
3. PricewaterhouseCoopers
4. Procter & Gamble
5. KPMG
6. Civil Service
7. Army
8. Unilever
9. Mars
10. BBC

2001
1. Accenture
2. Arthur Andersen
3. PricewaterhouseCoopers
4. Procter & Gamble
5. Goldman Sachs
6. Civil Service
7. KPMG
8. Unilever
9. Army
10. Mars

2002
1. Accenture
2. PricewaterhouseCoopers
3. Andersen (formerly Arthur Andersen)
4. Civil Service
5. Army
6. KPMG
7. Unilever
8. Procter & Gamble
9. Goldman Sachs
10. Mars

2003
1. Civil Service
2. Accenture
3. PricewaterhouseCoopers
4. Army
5. KPMG
6. HSBC
7. BBC
8. Procter & Gamble
9. NHS
10. Deloitte & Touche (now Deloitte)

2004
1. PricewaterhouseCoopers
2. Civil Service
3. Accenture
4. KPMG
5. NHS
6. BBC
7. Army
8. Procter & Gamble
9. HSBC
10. Deloitte

2005
1. PricewaterhouseCoopers
2. Civil Service
3. Accenture
4. KPMG
5. BBC
6. Deloitte
7. NHS
8. HSBC
9. Goldman Sachs
10. Procter & Gamble

2006
1. PricewaterhouseCoopers
2. Deloitte
3. KPMG
4. Civil Service
5. BBC
6. NHS
7. HSBC
8. Accenture
9. Procter & Gamble
10. Goldman Sachs

2007
1. PricewaterhouseCoopers
2. Deloitte
3. KPMG
4. Civil Service
5. BBC
6. NHS
7. Accenture
8. HSBC
9. Aldi
10. Goldman Sachs

2008
1. PricewaterhouseCoopers
2. Deloitte
3. KPMG
4. Accenture
5. NHS
6. Civil Service
7. BBC
8. Aldi
9. Teach First
10. Goldman Sachs

Source **The UK Graduate Careers Survey 1999-2008**, High Fliers Research Ltd, based on interviews with 146,419 students.

On a smarter planet,
the question isn't what can we do.
The question is what will we do?
Let's build a smarter planet.
ibm.com/start/uk

Where will my job experience really boost my career?

To find out about careers at Siemens go to page 206.

Siemens offers great opportunities to highly motivated people.

No matter what your professional goals may be, it's a tradition at Siemens to promote excellent work and to develop talent further. To ensure that we remain one of the leading innovators in the Industry, Energy and Healthcare Sectors, we are looking for people from all kinds of professions who want to make their next career move. Apply today.

siemens.co.uk/grad

SIEMENS

THE TIMES
TOP 100
GRADUATE EMPLOYERS

Index

	Accountancy	Consulting	Engineering	Finance	General Management	Human Resources	Investment Banking	IT	Law	Logistics	Manufacturing	Marketing	Media	Purchasing	Research & Development	Retailing	Sales	Other
BM	●	●		●	●			●							●			
J.P. Morgan				●			●	●										
John Lewis Partnership				●	●										●	●		
KPMG	●			●		●		●										
L'Oréal											●	●				●		
Lidl				●										●		●	●	
Linklaters									●									
Lloyds Banking Group				●	●	●		●										
Lovells									●									
Marks & Spencer								●						●		●		
Mars			●	●	●									●	●	●		
McDonald's Restaurants					●									●				
McKinsey & Company		●																
Metaswitch Networks								●										
Metropolitan Police	●		●	●	●			●				●	●		●			
MI5 – The Security Service			●	●		●		●										
Microsoft								●				●				●		
Ministry of Defence			●					●										
Morgan Stanley					●		●											
Network Rail	●		●	●	●			●							●			●
NGDP for Local Government					●													
NHS				●	●	●		●										
npower			●	●	●			●										
nucleargraduates		●	●	●						●				●				
Oxfam	●			●		●		●				●	●			●		
Police HPDS																		●
PricewaterhouseCoopers	●	●		●					●									
Procter & Gamble	●			●		●		●		●				●		●		
QinetiQ			●	●										●				
Rolls-Royce			●	●	●					●				●		●		
Royal Bank of Scotland Group	●			●	●			●							●	●		
Royal Navy			●	●	●	●		●	●	●								
Sainsbury's			●	●	●			●		●		●				●		
Shell			●	●	●			●										
Siemens			●	●	●			●										
Sky	●				●			●				●						
Slaughter and May									●									
Teach First	●	●	●	●	●	●		●	●	●		●	●		●	●		
Tesco	●	●	●	●	●			●		●		●		●		●	●	
Transport for London	●		●	●	●	●		●				●				●		
UBS	●		●	●	●		●	●										
Unilever			●	●	●									●		●		●
WPP Group												●	●					

High performance. Delivered.

Vacancies for around 300 graduates in 2010

 Consulting

 IT

Starting salary for 2010
£31,000
Plus £10k bonus in the first year.

Universities Accenture plans to visit in 2009-10
Aston, Bath, Birmingham, Bristol, Cambridge, Cardiff, Durham, Edinburgh, Exeter, Lancaster, Leeds, Leicester, London, Loughborough, Manchester, Newcastle, Nottingham, Oxford, Sheffield, Southampton, St Andrews, Strathclyde, Warwick, York
Please check with your university careers service for details of events.

Application deadline
Year-round recruitment

Contact Details
✉ ukgraduates@accenture.com
☎ 0500 100 189

Turn to page 224 now to request more information or visit our new website at www.top100graduateemployers.com

Achieve more.

accenture.com/ukgraduates

At Accenture, high performance is an everyday reality of working for a global management consulting, technology services and outsourcing company. This is a 177,000-strong organisation that looks for graduates who want to build an exceptional career in the world of business and technology.

Accenture gives high-performing graduates everything they need to achieve more. A consulting career begins with exceptional training, including a two-week course at Accenture's offices in Chicago within a graduate's first six months, and continues with the help of mentors, a combination of classroom and online training courses. Working with big-name clients and people at all levels across the business, graduates gain exposure and responsibility.

In the Analyst Consulting Group, they work on projects across industries and specialisms to build strong business and technology expertise. This equips them with the insight to deliver commercial benefits in management consulting, systems integration and technology, often working alongside outsourcing teams. Consulting with Accenture offers a real breadth and depth of experience.

Accenture works with clients to help them become high-performing businesses, and it needs similar qualities in its graduates. Good academics are essential – a 2:1 or above and at least 340 UCAS points. This must be complemented by further evidence of high performance, be it through work experience or community involvement, a position of leadership or responsibility, a real interest in technology, and a genuine career focus.

Achieve more with Accenture. Find out about their graduate opportunities, as well as their schemes and placements, at accenture.com/ukgraduates

AIRBUS

Vacancies for around 50-80 graduates in 2010

- Engineering
- Finance
- Human Resources
- IT
- Logistics
- Manufacturing
- Purchasing
- Research & Development

Starting salary for 2010
c.£24,500

Universities that Airbus plans to visit in 2009-10
Bath, Belfast, Bristol, Cambridge, Liverpool, Loughborough, Manchester, Nottingham, Sheffield, Southampton, Strathclyde, Warwick
Please check with your university careers service for details of events.

Application deadline
See website for full details.

Contact Details
☎ airbusuk-grad@airbus.com
Turn to page 224 now to request more information or visit our new website at www.top100graduateemployers.com

Over the past 40 years, Airbus has played a key role in the international air transport industry's evolution.

The recent introduction of Airbus' 21st century flagship A380 marked a new era. Not only is it setting new passenger comfort standards, the aircraft is raising the bar for environmental standards with its low fuel consumption and noise levels, as well as reduced emissions. The extra wide bodied A350 XWB, which will enter service in 2013, will continue to incorporate Airbus innovation and eco-efficiency principles, utilising new and advanced composite technologies to improve efficiency and reduce environmental impact.

Airbus offers exciting challenges for talented people in engineering and business focused roles to join a vibrant business; helping to continue to push the boundaries and to create an exciting, sustainable, eco-efficient future for aviation.

Collaborative and innovative graduates will enjoy the chance to develop their technical and leadership skills on the Airbus Direct Entry Graduate (DEG) programme. The structured programme helps develop a detailed knowledge of the chosen business function through placements in the UK and Europe, with strategic partners, customers and suppliers. Individual programmes can vary depending on the function joined.

Airbus DEGs have access to excellent focused training and support to help them achieve membership of professional institutions, further qualifications and long-term career planning. Airbus encourages a work-life balance with flexible working. Involvement in education and community projects, to broaden project management skills, is also part of the programme.

ALDI

www.aldirecruitment.co.uk

Vacancies for around
90-120 graduates in 2010

■ **General Management**
■ **Retailing**

Starting salary for 2010
£40,000
Rising to £60,000 after three years.

Universities that Aldi
plans to visit in 2009-10

Birmingham, Bristol, Cardiff, Dublin, Durham, Edinburgh, Glasgow, Leeds, Liverpool, London, Manchester, Newcastle, Nottingham, Sheffield, Southampton
Please check with your university careers service for details of events.

Application deadline
Year-round recruitment

Contact Details

Turn to page 224 now to request more information or visit our new website at www.top100graduateemployers.com

Looking for a challenging yet rewarding career with outstanding prospects for progression and success? As Aldi grows as a business it continues to attract the country's top graduates to join the unrivalled Graduate Training Area Management Programme.

Aldi's market leading package provides graduates with comprehensive training for the role of Area Manager covering all aspects of retail management, from store operations through to financial administration, logistics and property management. The programme promotes the development of leadership skills, commercial awareness, technical and managerial skills whilst providing a strong focus on customer satisfaction and business efficiency.

Graduate trainees also have the opportunity to manage a store within weeks, progressing quickly to managing a multi-million pound area of four to six stores as if it were their own business. With the opportunity of a two year secondment in Europe or further afield plus a chance of directorship after five years, Aldi stands out from other retailers in giving its graduates high levels of responsibility from day one.

Graduates who can demonstrate that they can apply themselves outside the working environment will make a big impact when applying for the scheme. Aldi is looking for graduates who are determined team players with the need to be competitive, motivated and the desire to succeed. Offering variety, ownership and career satisfaction, the company is looking for confident, ambitious and enthusiastic individuals with a hunger for career success.

Are you the class of 2010?

Approximately 500,000 students will graduate this academic year (more than ever before). The big question is, can you stand head and shoulders above this huge crowd? If you're positive the answer's 'yes', then you could be one of the real class acts of 2010. And you could secure your place on the award-winning Aldi Graduate Area Management Training Programme.

We're looking for people with exceptional drive. Ambition and determination. We'll want to see you can grab the opportunity to take on real responsibility. (In fact, we'll expect you to be managing four to six Aldi stores – single-handedly – within months of joining us).

So, can you answer the big question and make the most of this unparalleled opportunity for success with one of the world's largest, privately owned companies? Let us know now by going to **www.aldirecruitment.co.uk**

Graduate
Area Manager
£40,000

rising to
£60,000
after three years

Fully expensed
Audi A4

Opportunity
for directorship
within 5 years

International
secondment
opportunities

ALLEN & OVERY

www.allenovery.com/careeruk

Vacancies for around 105 graduates in 2010
For training contracts starting in 2012

Law

Starting salary for 2010
£38,000

Universities Allen & Overy plans to visit in 2009-10
Belfast, Birmingham, Bristol, Cambridge, Cardiff, City, Dublin, Durham, East Anglia, Edinburgh, Exeter, Glasgow, Kent, Lancaster, Leeds, Leicester, London, Manchester, Newcastle, Northumbria, Nottingham, Oxford, Reading, Sheffield, Southampton, Warwick, York
Please check with your university careers service for details of events.

Application deadline
See website for full details.

Contact Details
graduate.recruitment@allenovery.com
020 3088 0000

Turn to page 224 now to request more information or visit our new website at www.top100graduateemployers.com

Allen & Overy is an international legal practice with over 5,000 people in 31 major centres worldwide. The practice's client list includes many of the world's top businesses, financial institutions and governments.

Allen & Overy is world renowned for the high quality of its banking, corporate and international capital markets advice, but also has major strengths in dispute resolution, employment and benefits, tax, and real estate.

Within its broad range of expertise, the practice offers a training contract characterised by flexibility and choice. Training contracts are tailored for each trainee to ensure they have the best start to their career. Given the strength of the practice's international finance practice, trainees spend at least 12 months working in banking, corporate and international capital markets, with contentious experience in either dispute resolution or employment. There are also opportunities for trainees to undertake an international or client secondment in their second year of training. By working closely with trainers and other colleagues, trainees develop practical experience and enjoy a high level of early responsibility.

Vital to Allen & Overy's success is the way they approach work. Allen & Overy people enjoy what they do and want to employ people who have initiative while maintaining a professional, supportive and friendly working environment.

Allen & Overy recruits 105 trainee solicitors and 65 vacation students (winter and summer) each year.

Applications are welcome from both law and non-law candidates. At least a 2.1 degree (or equivalent) should be predicted or acheived, with evidence of teamwork, leadership, motivation, and problem-solving demonstrated.

▲ Arcadia Group Limited

Vacancies for around
150-200 **graduates in 2010**

■ Finance
■ Human Resources
■ Retailing

Starting salary for 2010
£17,500-£23,000

Universities that the Arcadia Group plans to visit in 2009-10
London
Please check with your university careers service for details of events.

Application deadline
Year-round recruitment

Contact Details
Turn to page 224 now to request more information or visit our new website at www.top100graduateemployers.com

The Arcadia Group is the UK's largest privately owned fashion retailer with over 28,000 employees, 2,700 outlets and over 400 international stores in 29 different countries. Arcadia's portfolio of brands include seven of the best known high street fashion brands – Burton, Dorothy Perkins, Evans, Miss Selfridge, Topman, Topshop and Wallis – along with the shopping concept Outfit.

Arcadia offers a wide variety of different careers for graduates and trainees. London based opportunities include; Buying, Merchandising, Distribution, Finance and HR. Their Retail Management programme offers candidates nationwide opportunities.

Arcadia's people play a vital part in their success and they're committed to supporting the development of their teams. In all roles, graduates will benefit from on the job competency based training and core skills workshops. Graduates and trainees are rewarded with a competitive salary, up to 25 days holiday, bonus, membership of the group pension scheme, sponsorship of professional qualifications and an attractive 25% discount on products from Arcadia stores!

They are always on the look out for the most commercial, passionate, success driven candidates that have passion for customer service and fashion retail. Ideal backgrounds differ for each role, but all applications will benefit from relevant work experience.

Arcadia's Buying, Merchandising and Distribution roles are recruited all year round, while the Finance, HR and Retail Management programmes are open for applications from early September 2009.

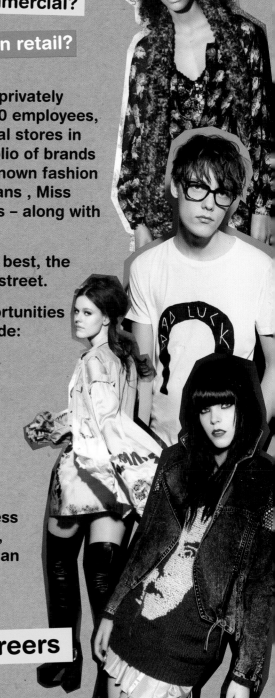

ARUP

www.arup.com

Vacancies for around 120 graduates in 2010

■ Consulting
■ Engineering

Vacancies also available in Europe, Asia and the USA.

Starting salary for 2010
£24,000

Universities that Arup plans to visit in 2009-10
Bath, Belfast, Birmingham, Bristol, Cambridge, Cardiff, Durham, Edinburgh, Heriot-Watt, Leeds, Liverpool, Manchester, Newcastle, Nottingham, Sheffield, Strathclyde, Warwick
Please check with your university careers service for details of events.

Application deadline
Year-round recruitment

Contact Details
✉ gradrec@arup.com

Turn to page 224 now to request more information or visit our new website at www.top100graduateemployers.com

Arup is a global firm of designers, engineers, planners and business consultants providing a diverse range of professional services to clients around the world. Arup's innovative and fully-integrated approach brings their full complement of skills and knowledge to bear on any given design problem.

They exert a significant influence on the built environment and are the creative force behind many of the world's most innovative and sustainable designs. Examples of Arup projects are: the Beijing National Stadium and National Aquatics Centre, Sydney Opera House, the Millennium Bridge, the Swiss Re Headquarters and the City of Manchester Stadium.

Arup has almost 9,000 staff working in 92 offices in more than 37 countries. At any one time, they have over 10,000 projects running concurrently.

A commitment to the environment and the communities being worked in has always been at the heart of the Arup ethos. It defines their approach to their work, to their clients and collaborators, and to each other.

Their ethos is summarised in the aims of the firm, set out by Ove Arup in his key speech of 1970. Arup will ensure that the Arup name is always associated with quality; they will act honestly and fairly in dealing with their staff and others; and they will enhance prosperity for all Arup staff.

Arup recruits over 120 graduates in the UK every year and has graduate vacancies in architecture, engineering and planning roles, there are also vacancies throughout the rest of the world.

For further information please visit www.arup.com

ASDA

**Vacancies for around
52 graduates in 2010**

- Finance
- General Management
- IT
- Logistics
- Purchasing
- Retailing

Starting salary for 2010
£23,000

**Universities that Asda
plans to visit in 2009-10**
Bradford, Brunel, Hull,
Lancaster, Leeds,
Leicester, Loughborough,
Manchester, Nottingham,
Nottingham Trent,
Sheffield, York
Please check with your university
careers service for details of events.

Application deadline
1st March 2010

Contact Details
Turn to page 224 now to request more
information or visit our new website at
www.top100graduateemployers.com

Part of the Wal-Mart family, Asda is one of the UK's fastest
growing, and most successful retailers employing over 170,000
colleagues across nearly 400 stores, 25 depots and its head
office, Asda House.

Asda graduates play a pivotal role in ensuring the expectations of more than
17 million customers are exceeded each week. For example, they could
become a store manager and learn how to inspire up to 700 colleagues,
or they could be part of the trading floor, negotiating with suppliers from the
UK to the Far East to deliver every day low prices to Asda's customers.
There are numerous opportunities for graduates to gain invaluable exposure
to the exciting projects that keep Asda at the cutting edge of retail.

Asda also ensures it creates a thriving work environment for its colleagues.
The organisation is proud of its unique culture which encourages graduates
to reach their potential as quickly as possible and enjoy themselves
along the way. Their achievements will be recognised and their feedback
encouraged. These are just a few of the reasons why Asda was named
'Innovative Employer of the Year' at this year's prestigious Oracle Retail
Week Awards.

Asda welcomes all types of degree and its graduate programme covers a
variety of areas from Retail Management, Trading, Ecommerce and Finance
to Property and Construction, IT Management and Distribution Management.

Whatever the area, graduates take on early responsibility and make a real
contribution to the business as they develop the skills they'll need to become
a future leader at Asda.

THINK BEYOND

Is retail all black and white? Is it all barcodes and boxes, scanning and sorting? Or is there something more? Something complex, colourful, intriguing, vibrant? Something sustainable, inspiring and full of endless possibilities? Something that could take you further than most other graduate careers could? Think beyond the barcode. Think Asda and visit www.ASDA.jobs/graduates

ASDA SAVING YOU MONEY EVERY DAY

AstraZeneca

Vacancies for around 15-25 graduates in 2010

- Engineering
- Finance
- IT
- Logistics
- Marketing
- Purchasing
- Research & Development

AstraZeneca
wants to
make a
difference.

One of the world's leading pharmaceutical companies, AstraZeneca turns great ideas into innovative medicines which make real difference to peoples lives.

The company's excellent reputation and diversity of graduate opportunities make them the natural choice for candidates from a science background. However, their strengths in manufacturing and commerce mean they can also provide challenges to graduates from other disciplines. Whatever their degree subject, graduates will be excited by the quality and diversity of opportunity. Programmes are designed to progress careers through an integrated range of flexible training activities and blended learning ideas.

From day-one induction and personal mentoring to management and global leadership programmes, AstraZeneca provides the resources and support graduates need to reach their full potential; while cross-functional moves, secondments and international assignments can broaden the experience. It's a performance-based culture with competitive salaries and bonuses that are linked to overall progress. But they also believe that quality of life and quality of work go hand in hand. That's why they actively pursue opportunities for flexible working arrangements.

Core benefits include a minimum level of pension contribution and healthcare provision, and the additional range of 'rewards options' is considerable. But these are benefits that people tend to appreciate further down the line. What probably excites graduates more at this stage is the opportunity to develop their skills within a truly global business that's setting the standards in an industry rich in challenges and rewards.

Starting salary for 2010
£25,000-£28,000

Universities AstraZeneca plans to visit in 2009-10
Please check with your university careers service for details of events.

Application deadline
Year-round recruitment
See website for full details.

Contact Details
Turn to page 224 now to request more information or visit our new website at www.top100graduateemployers.com

ATKINS

Vacancies for around 150 graduates in 2010

- Consulting
- Engineering
- Finance

Starting salary for 2010
£20,000-£28,000

Universities that Atkins plans to visit in 2009-10
Aberdeen, Bath, Belfast, Birmingham, Bristol, Cambridge, Cardiff, Durham, Glasgow, Heriot-Watt, Leeds, Liverpool, London, Loughborough, Manchester, Newcastle, Nottingham, Oxford, Sheffield, Southampton, Strathclyde, Surrey, Sussex, Swansea, Warwick
Please check with your university careers service for details of events.

Application deadline
11th January 2010

Contact Details
✉ graduates@atkinsglobal.com
☎ 0121 483 6233

Turn to page 224 now to request more information or visit our new website at www.top100graduateemployers.com

Atkins is a multinational design and engineering consultancy, providing expertise to help resolve complex challenges in the built and natural environment. Whether it's the concept for a new landmark building, improving major public transport systems, helping to clean up the UK nuclear industry or the improvement of a management process, Atkins plan, design and enable solutions. They're also proud to be pioneers in Carbon Critical Design, putting sustainability at the heart of every design question.

The cutting edge projects Atkins is working on have a real impact on people's lives. Take their visionary remodelling of Birmingham New Street station. Or their back-to-basics approach to helping people move freely around Oxford Circus. Then there's 'Anaconda', a 200 metre long tube that creates electricity by 'pulsing' under the sea – a real breakthrough in renewable energy.

The Atkins Graduate Development Programme is designed to give graduates choices about how their career unfolds. They'll work on influential projects alongside some of the brightest industry experts to achieve their chosen professional accreditation. They'll also get support from a mentor, as well as the Atkins graduate community.

Atkins is in The Sunday Times 20 Best Big Companies to Work For in the UK and, for the fourth year running, Atkins was voted Most Popular Graduate Recruiter in Construction and Civil Engineering at the TARGET National Graduate Recruitment Awards. They're also proud to feature again in the Top 50 Places Where Women Want to Work.

Visit www.atkinsglobal.com/graduates/times to find out more and apply.

ATKINS

Aerospace
Architecture
Building Design
Communication & Systems
Conventional Power
Defence
Environment
Finance
Geotechnics & Tunnelling
Highways
Intelligent Transport Systems
Management Consultancy
Nuclear Power
Oil & Gas
Rail & Metro
Transport Planning
Water

Aim higher

Join our Graduate Development Programme and together we'll build a brighter future for everyone. Instead of leading you down a set career path, we'll open doors by giving you choices about how your career unfolds and providing a breadth of projects to gain experience on. And as one of the leading infrastructure consultancies, we're well placed to invest in your development and offer the career opportunities you're looking for.

If you share our boundless curiosity and drive to improve the world in which we all live, work and play, it's a chance to become an expert in whatever inspires you most.

Make the story of your career a more interesting one. To find out more and apply, visit **www.atkinsglobal.com/graduates/times**

Plan Design Enable

BAE SYSTEMS

REAL PERFORMANCE. REAL ADVANTAGE.

www.baesystems.com/graduates

Vacancies for around 250-300 graduates in 2010

- Engineering
- Finance
- General Management
- Human Resources
- Manufacturing
- Purchasing
- Research & Development
- Sales

Starting salary for 2010
£24,000-£28,000

Universities BAE Systems plans to visit in 2009-10

Bath, Belfast, Bristol, Brunel, Cambridge, Cardiff, Durham, Edinburgh, Glasgow, Heriot-Watt, Kent, Lancaster, Leeds, Liverpool, Loughborough, Manchester, Newcastle, Nottingham, Oxford, Sheffield, Southampton, Strathclyde, Surrey, Warwick, York
Please check with your university careers service for details of events.

Application deadline
Year-round recruitment

Contact Details
Turn to page 224 now to request more information or visit our new website at www.top100graduateemployers.com

BAE Systems is the premier global defence and aerospace company delivering a full range of products and services for air, land and naval forces, as well as advanced electronics, information technology solutions and customer support services. With 106,000 highly skilled people, and customers in over 100 countries, BAE Systems' sales exceed £18.5 billion.

In the exciting arena of international defence, BAE Systems offers a wealth of opportunities for both graduates and undergraduates.

BAE Systems has three graduate entry programmes; GDF is the main programme, FLDP for those looking for a finance leadership career and Sigma for fast track international leadership.

Most graduates will join the Graduate Development Framework (GDF), which is a two-year scheme. Successful applicants will receive on-the-job training from some of the most talented people in their industry. They will work on real projects offering real responsibility.

Line managers work closely with graduates to develop and track an ongoing plan for personal development. Graduates may well receive opportunities for secondments to different sites and projects, to give them greater exposure to the business in line with development objectives. When it's appropriate, BAE Systems will also give successful applicants all the resources and support they need to achieve relevant professional qualifications.

To find out more about BAE Systems' projects, opportunities and entry requirements, please visit www.baesystems.com/graduates where application forms can be submitted.

CALLING ALL OF NATURE'S GREAT PERFORMERS.

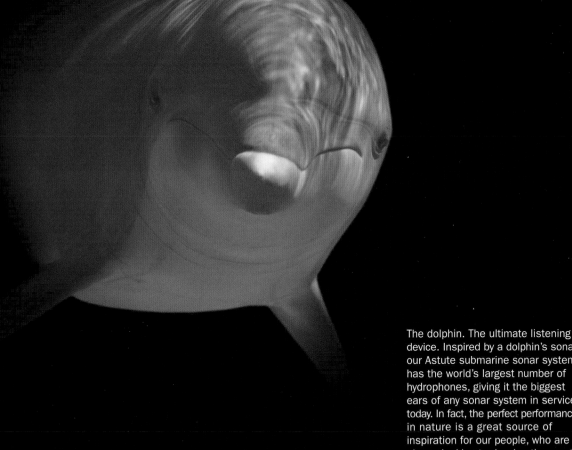

The dolphin. The ultimate listening device. Inspired by a dolphin's sonar, our Astute submarine sonar system has the world's largest number of hydrophones, giving it the biggest ears of any sonar system in service today. In fact, the perfect performance in nature is a great source of inspiration for our people, who are always looking to develop the most effective defence, aerospace and security systems on earth.

BUSINESS | ENGINEERING | FINANCE

BAE SYSTEMS

baesystems.com/graduates

REAL PERFORMANCE. REAL ADVANTAGE.

Bank of America Merrill Lynch

Vacancies for around 250 graduates in 2010

- Finance
- Human Resources
- Investment Banking
- IT
- Marketing
- Research & Development
- Sales

Vacancies also available in Europe.

Starting salary for 2010
£Competitive

Universities that Bank of America Merrill Lynch plans to visit in 2009-10
Cambridge, City, Durham, Lancaster, Liverpool, London, Manchester, Oxford, Warwick
Please check with your university careers service for details of events.

Application deadline
6th November 2009

Contact Details
Turn to page 224 now to request more information or visit our new website at www.top100graduateemployers.com

Bank of America and Merrill Lynch have joined forces, creating a combined organisation that brings together two companies that complement each other in the investment banking, global markets, research and wealth management businesses.

The combined size, scale and global presence of the organisation give it the ability to deliver a wider breadth of world-class products and services to clients. With a leading wealth management franchise and a premier corporate and investment banking and capital markets business, the company is well-equipped to meet the evolving financial environment and well-positioned to compete globally.

Full-time and internship programmes are offered in the following areas: Global Markets, Global Investment Banking, Global Wealth & Investment Management, Research, Global Product Solutions, Risk Management, Technology, Human Resources and Europe Card Services. Students who join the organisation gain a breadth of knowledge and experience and are positioned for great growth opportunities.

Graduates who join gain experience working alongside professionals who are leaders in the industry and skilled mentors committed to developing talent. An analyst has unlimited opportunities to develop abilities and grow professionally through a variety of structured training courses.

Strong academic qualifications and quantitative skills are important for success in our analyst programmes. Equally important are initiative, strategic and creative thinking, communication skills and a genuine interest in the financial markets.

Choose. Connect. Grow.

Choose to work in an entrepreneurial culture where you will connect with high-profile clients and grow your career through valuable mentoring from senior financial services professionals. Whether your interest is in Global Markets, Investment Banking, Global Wealth & Investment Management, Research, Global Product Solutions, Risk Management, Technology, Human Resources or Card Services, our career opportunities are second to none.

bankofamerica.com/campusrecruiting

Bank of America
Merrill Lynch

BARCLAYS

www.inspiredbybarclays.com

**Vacancies for around
150 graduates in 2010**

- Accountancy
- Finance
- General Management
- Human Resources
- IT
- Marketing
- Retailing
- Sales

Starting salary for 2010
£Competitive

**Universities that Barclays
plans to visit in 2009-10**
Bath, Cambridge,
Cardiff, City, Durham,
Edinburgh, Exeter, Leeds,
Loughborough, Manchester,
Nottingham, Oxford,
St Andrews, Warwick
Please check with your university
careers service for details of events.

Application deadline
31st December 2009

Contact Details
✉ barclays.graduates@reed.co.uk
Turn to page 224 now to request more
information or visit our new website at
www.top100graduateemployers.com

TO GO FURTHER,

Barclays spirit of innovation inspires groundbreaking ideas that move the entire industry forward. Whether it's reaching untapped markets, capitalising on the latest technology, launching futuristic new retail bank branches or introducing imaginative products like the carbon-neutral debit card, Barclays always seem to get there first. Not surprisingly their fresh-thinking approach also makes them an inspirational place to develop a graduate career.

That could be in Barclaycard, Commercial Bank, Finance, HR, Retail Banking, Technology, Tax or UKRB Marketing & Products. Each business area runs its own structured training programme lasting between one and three years. Graduates will get a real insight into how the area operates, enjoy a high profile and learn from business leaders.

Barclays look for a strong academic background. But the right attitude is just as important as a quick brain. Graduates must be ambitious, commercially aware and focused with the drive and initiative to improve on what's gone before. What has been done outside of academia – placements, gap years, voluntary work or sporting or cultural activities for example – will also help Barclays decide whether applicants have the potential to make a real impact on their business.

Expect formal training, on-the-job learning, study leave to help gain professional qualifications and a personal budget to invest in personal development that's relevant to the role. What's more, graduate development won't stop when the programme ends. Career-long learning is a way of life at Barclays and will encourage successful applicants to really make a mark and get on.

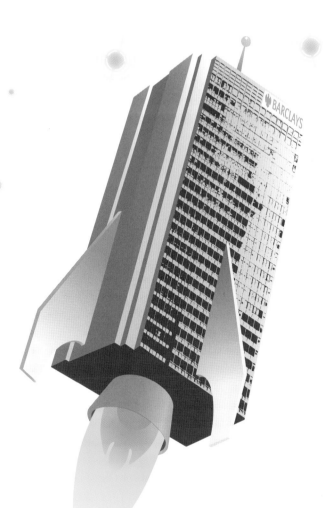

START IN THE RIGHT PLACE

We make stars rocket. We have to. Only by developing the brightest people will we have the accomplished leaders we need to take our business to even greater heights. So if you're always wondering how to do things better, come and help keep us ahead of the market. People like you, who know good ideas when they see them or can come up with them in the first place, are the reason we're behind so many industry firsts. And why we're always getting better at everything we do – from product development to social responsibility projects to helping you get ahead. Wherever you join us, we'll push you to push us. Pretty inspiring stuff.

Graduate careers in Barclaycard, Commercial Bank, Finance, HR, Retail Banking, Tax, Technology, UKRB Marketing and Products

www.inspiredbybarclays.com

BARCLAYS CAPITAL

Vacancies for around 200 graduates in 2010

- Finance
- Human Resources
- Investment Banking
- IT
- Law
- Marketing

Vacancies also available in Europe, the USA and Asia.

Starting salary for 2010
£Competitive

Universities that Barclays Capital plans to visit in 2009-10
Bath, Birmingham, Bristol, Cambridge, Durham, Edinburgh, London, Manchester, Nottingham, Oxford, Reading, Southampton, Warwick
Please check with your university careers service for details of events.

Application deadline
15th November 2009

Contact Details
Turn to page 224 now to request more information or visit our new website at www.top100graduateemployers.com

Barclays Capital is the investment banking division of Barclays Bank PLC, offering strategic advisory, financing and risk management solutions to large corporate, government and institutional clients.

Barclays Capital has more than 20,000 people in offices around the world, and has the global reach and distribution power to meet the needs of issuers and investors in all the major financial markets. Graduate and internship opportunities are offered in areas right across the firm, both in front office roles such as Investment Banking, Sales and Trading, and also infrastructure areas such as Technology, Marketing & Human Resources.

The graduate programme is the key to the success of Barclays Capital. Senior managers across the firm are intrinsically involved in graduate training, giving graduates a remarkable degree of insight and exposure from the moment they join. The programme starts with an intensive introduction to the firm, their products, instruments and services, and the wider financial markets. Graduates will gain more than a theoretical understanding, with a variety of case studies, workshops and presentations giving invaluable practical knowledge. They can also expect comprehensive role-specific training, plus soft skills development.

As well as full-time opportunities, 10-12 week summer internships are offered and off-cycle opportunities, depending on business need. In all cases, interns will find themselves at the heart of the action. They'll gain real experience in a real role, working on anything from live transactions and marketing projects to research and analysis, depending on the business area. As well as benefiting from extensive training before and during the programme, there are opportunities to network with intern colleagues, recent graduates and senior members of the firm.

EXPECT TO GO PLACES
YOU NEVER EXPECTED.

**Graduate careers in
investment banking**

Here at Barclays Capital, we'll help you
fulfil your highest ambitions in the
most unexpected ways. For instance,
we think the best way for you to get to
the top is to learn from the people who
are already there. That's why our
senior managers are intrinsically
involved in training our graduates –
and why you can look forward to
extraordinary insights and top-floor
views from day one. It's time to raise
your expectations. Visit our website
to find out more.

barcap.com/expectexcellence

Expect Excellence

BBC

www.bbc.co.uk/jobs

Possible Vacancies in 2010

- Engineering
- Finance
- General Management
- IT
- Law
- Marketing
- Media
- Research & Development

Starting salary for 2010
£Competitive

Universities that the BBC plans to visit in 2009-10
Please check with your university careers service for details of events.

Application deadline
Year-round recruitment

Contact Details
✉ hr@bbchrdirect.co.uk
☎ 0370 333 1330

Turn to page 224 now to request more information or visit our new website at www.top100graduateemployers.com

The BBC is one of the world's best-known broadcasting brands and today's digital BBC plays a key role in modern life. As an organisation funded by the universal licence fee, the BBC's mission is to inform, educate and entertain. Its content reaches over 60 million people in the UK (not to mention millions more around the globe). It is watched, listened to, read and interacted with via 10 television services, 57 radio stations, its award winning website and via the Red Button too.

In this new digital, on-demand world, the BBC's role is changing from a one-way, studio-based broadcaster of programmes, into an audience focused 'anytime, anywhere, anyhow', content brand. New services, like iPlayer, are strengthening this change in direction and maintaining the BBC's place at the forefront of the broadcasting world.

This forward-thinking approach extends beyond its services. The BBC is creating an environment that's friendly, welcoming and open to change. One that's as diverse as it is fast-moving, and where challenge, development and recognition go hand-in-hand.

However, while the atmosphere is relaxed, the ethic here is very hard working and there's a real focus on development at every level. So whether graduates join through one of the variety of training schemes that the BBC advertise throughout the year or by applying for a specific vacancy, they will find the right inspiration to bring their career to life.

To find out more about working at the BBC and to search and apply for current vacancies, visit bbc.co.uk/jobs

BBC RADIO 5 live

BBC TWO

BBC RADIO 1Xtra

BBC | cymru wales

cbbc BBC

BBC RADIO 3 90–93 FM

BBC NEWS

BBC RADIO ASIAN NETWORK

BBC RADIO 5 live sports extra

BBC iPlayer

BBC WORLD SERVICE

BBC

BBC RADIO 4 92–95 FM

BBC RADIO 2

BBC Scotland

BBC FOUR

BBC NORTHERN IRELAND

BBC three

BBC RADIO 7

BBC RADIO 6 music

BBC SPORT

BBC RADIO 1

BBC one

BDO Stoy Hayward

Vacancies for around
150 graduates in 2010

■ Accountancy

■ Finance

Starting salary for 2010
£Competitive

Universities that
BDO Stoy Hayward
plans to visit in 2009-10

Aston, Bath, Birmingham,
Bristol, Cambridge, Cardiff,
Durham, Glasgow, Leeds,
London, Loughborough,
Manchester, Nottingham,
Oxford, Reading, Sheffield,
Southampton, Strathclyde,
Surrey, Warwick
Please check with your university
careers service for details of events.

Application deadline
Year-round recruitment

Contact Details

✉ student.recruitment@bdo.co.uk

☎ 020 7893 2085

Turn to page 224 now to request more
information or visit our new website at
www.top100graduateemployers.com

WHAT IF THE SECRET OF SUCCESS WASN'T A SECRET?

BDO Stoy Hayward is the UK Member Firm of BDO International, the world's fifth largest accountancy network with more than 1,000 offices (including exclusive alliances of BDO Member Firms) in over 100 countries. They specialise in helping businesses, whether start-ups, mid-tiers or multi-nationals, to achieve their goals. Their objective is to help their clients maximise their potential.

They have their own very special culture. One that people enjoy working in, no matter what their background, age, sex or ethnicity. They want individuals who are bright and creative – who place importance on living their values. They also care about sustainability. This is why they have developed a strong corporate social responsibility programme that encourages graduates to 'give something back' to the community, by volunteering and considering their impact on the environment.

Their strength in the marketplace is mirrored in their recent awards which include the Financial Times Best Workplace UK and The Sunday Times 100 Best Companies to Work For.

At BDO Stoy Hayward, every day prepares graduates for the next. Graduates will attend external tutor firms for their professional training, but BDO Stoy Hayward will make sure they have all the study and revision time they need, as well as in-house support and extra tuition if they want it. Their results are excellent.

In addition to an excellent technical knowledge and know-how programme, BDO Stoy Hayward have designed leadership and management development skills programmes and solutions which are designed to help graduates 'widen their perspective'.

WHAT IF PEOPLE ASKED HOW YOU WERE AND REALLY WANTED TO KNOW?

BDO Stoy Hayward is the award winning UK Member Firm of BDO International, with more than 1,000 offices* in over 100 countries, it's an exciting time to join us with opportunities to grow with our success.

But our growth alone is not what makes us special. It's the open and supportive culture of our firm and in 2008 we were one of the FT Best Workplaces in the UK and in 2009, the highest new entry in the Times Top 100 Graduate Employers.

Apply online at www.bdo.co.uk/careers

YOU'LL NOTICE THE DIFFERENCE

'Tax Team of the Year' 2008
'Audit Team of the Year' 2008
'Corporate Finance Team of the Year' 2008

BDO Stoy Hayward
Accountants and Business Advisers

*including exclusive alliances of BDO member firms

Bloomberg

careers.bloomberg.com

Vacancies for around 250+ graduates in 2010

- Finance
- IT
- Media
- Research & Development
- Sales

Vacancies also available in the USA and Asia.

Starting salary for 2010
£Competitive
Plus benefits.

Universities Bloomberg plans to visit in 2009-10
Aston, Bath, Birmingham, Bristol, Cambridge, City, Durham, Edinburgh, Glasgow, Leeds, Liverpool, London, Loughborough, Manchester, Oxford, Reading, Sheffield, Southampton, Warwick, York
Please check with your university careers service for details of events.

Application deadline
Year-round recruitment

Contact Details
Turn to page 224 now to request more information or visit our new website at www.top100graduateemployers.com

Bloomberg is a leading global provider of data, news and analytics. The Bloomberg Professional® Service and Bloomberg's media services provide real-time and archived financial and market data, pricing, trading, news and communications tools in a single, integrated package.

Bloomberg's clients include corporations, news organisations, financial and legal professionals, and individuals around the world. With over 10,000 employees operating in more than 140 countries, Bloomberg is truly international. The largest offices include New York, London and Tokyo, and this is where the majority of graduate opportunities are located.

Graduate positions include financial sales, software development, global data, IT, project management, news and many more. For most roles, a second language is desirable but not essential. Bloomberg recruits all year round and from any discipline. A passion for finance, technology or an international career is required. Bloomberg breaks down barriers between people and encourages communication by bring colleagues together. With no job titles or executive areas, the culture fosters interaction at every level.

Bloomberg supports community programmes by reinvesting resources back into society through sponsorships and employee volunteer activities. But the real depth and diversity of Bloomberg's way of life comes from the creativity and commitment of its people. Training is extensive and ongoing via Bloomberg University. Courses are wide-ranging and available to all, allowing graduates to progress quickly and take on responsibility quickly. Opportunities are listed on the website and start dates are available throughout the year.

Bloomberg

MOVE THE MARKETS.
Innovate from the front.

Join the company at the forefront of finance and technology.

Bloomberg provides information to business leaders around the world. Our employees have a passion for excellence, no matter what their experience is. We foster that passion and encourage growth and development in every way possible.

We have opportunities in Financial Sales, Data Analysis, Software Development, News and many more areas. Bloomberg is the ideal place for you to develop your knowledge and enthusiasm for the financial markets. **Join Bloomberg.**

careers.bloomberg.com

BCG

THE BOSTON CONSULTING GROUP

www.bcg.com

Vacancies for around
30 graduates in 2010

■ Consulting

Vacancies also available elsewhere
in the world.

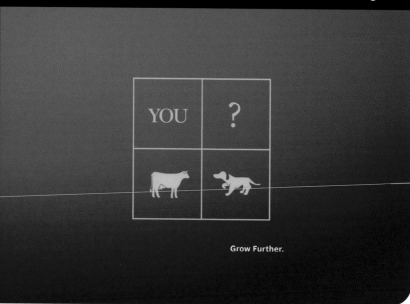

Grow Further.

Starting salary for 2010
£Competitive

Universities that
Boston Consulting Group
plans to visit in 2009-10
Cambridge, London, Oxford
Please check with your university
careers service for details of events.

Application deadline
6th November 2009

Contact Details
✉ lonrecruiting@bcg.com
☎ 020 7753 5353
Turn to page 224 now to request more
information or visit our new website at
www.top100graduateemployers.com

The Boston Consulting Group (BCG) is a global management consulting firm and the world's leading advisor on business strategy. BCG helps their clients achieve sustainable competitive advantage, build more capable organisations and secure lasting results. BCG customised approach combines deep insight into the dynamics of companies and markets with close collaboration at all levels in our clients' organisations.

New graduates can make a difference at BCG. They will collaborate daily with the world's leading businesses on a wide range of high-level strategic challenges. As a member of a team, their role will be to partner with clients in all sectors and regions to identify their highest-value opportunities, address their most critical challenges and transform their businesses. They will drive client results, helping leaders in business not just play better, but change the rules of the game.

BCG cares about personal growth. BCG employees can be sponsored through an MBA in a leading business school, choose a secondment with a world class client or work in one of many offices around the world. BCG's career development team offers employees the opportunity to be mentored, stretched and intellectually challenged. BCG's international training programme helps consultants develop a comprehensive toolkit of business and management skills.

BCG is winning. Since 1990 they have grown at an industry-beating 16 per cent annually. This record growth creates expansive opportunity for BCG's people: broader choices, faster learning and rapid advancement. They are looking for people to join and continue this success. Graduates with excellent analytical abilities balanced with impressive interpersonal skills, as well as drive and curiosity, can realise their potential at BCG.

Grow Further.

At BCG, your potential is limited only by your talents and ambitions. You will work daily with the world's leading businesses on a wide range of high-level strategic challenges. The knowledge, experience, and skills you'll gain will provide the springboard you need to excel in any field within BCG or beyond.

How far will you grow?

The Boston Consulting Group

bp

beyond petroleum

www.bp.com/ukgraduates

Vacancies for around 150 graduates in 2010

- Accountancy
- Engineering
- Finance
- Logistics

Starting salary for 2010
£Competitive

Universities that BP plans to visit in 2009-10

Bath, Birmingham, Cambridge, Leeds, London, Manchester, Nottingham, Oxford, Strathclyde
Please check with your university careers service for details of events.

Application deadline
Varies by function
See website for full details.

Contact Details
☎ 0800 279 2088

Turn to page 224 now to request more information or visit our new website at www.top100graduateemployers.com

BP's business is the exploration, production, refining, marketing, trading and distribution of energy, and they do it on a phenomenal scale. They own or part-own 17 refineries around the world, operate tens of thousands of miles of pipelines and run a fleet of more than 80 ships. They produce about 4 million barrels of oil equivalent per day and own world-leading brands, such as BP, Amoco, Aral and Castrol serving millions of customers each day. And in recent years, they've made profits of over $20 billion a year.

BP aims to meet a growing global demand for energy without compromising the planet. They are going further to produce cleaner fuels and develop new energies, and they're investing in the technology and people to do it. Every year BP commits over $1 billion to technology that is shaping the future of the industry; and every year they hire 750 graduates and interns globally to become managers and technical experts of the future.

BP recruits into engineering, science and business. There are many opportunities within these – from chemical engineering to geoscience, chemistry to finance, trading to drilling and completions engineering. Whichever team graduates join, they will find the same support and encouragement to achieve new professional heights – and beyond.

BP looks for drive, enthusiasm, ambition and the ability to think creatively and relate well to others. In addition to mobility and a relevant minimum 2:1 degree, successful applicants will possess strong influencing, analytical and technical skills. To find out more and to make an application please go to www.bp.com/ukgraduates

Do you have the energy we need?

Population growth, escalating energy demand, climate concern and energy security - these are some of the challenges BP faces.

From the world's largest oil platform in the Gulf of Mexico, to the science that enables us to see through millions of years of sand, shells and salt, to some of the most advanced refineries in the world, BP makes a difference to the world, every day.

The energy resource we rely on is our people. **Are you up for the challenge?**

bp.com/ukgraduates

official partner of the
Olympic and Paralympic Games

bp

beyond petroleum

Cadbury

Vacancies for around 15-20 graduates in 2010

- Engineering
- Finance
- Logistics
- Manufacturing
- Marketing
- Purchasing
- Sales

Starting salary for 2010
£26,000

Universities that Cadbury plans to visit in 2009-10
Please check with your university careers service for details of events.

Application deadline
15th November 2009

Contact Details
cadburygraduates@cadbury.com
Turn to page 224 now to request more information or visit our new website at www.top100graduateemployers.com

For over 200 years, Cadbury has been the name in chocolate and confectionery; making brands that people love; household names, fun, iconic brands that bring moments of pleasure to people the world over. Global market leaders, their advertising is award winning and their marketing is sharp and effective.

It's a place where careers are made, and reputations are built – an exciting, stimulating, challenging place to work. It's an organisation where high performance drives impressive growth, a modern, vibrant place with strong values at its heart.

Cadbury believe that great people make great products, so growth, development and opportunity are firmly embedded in their culture. That's why they take so much care to choose a handful of graduates to join their business.

Sales & Marketing graduates will identify and track consumer and market trends, strengthening brands and creating new ones.

Finance graduates will provide sound measurement and analysis to help make the right business decisions.

Supply chain graduates will enable profitable growth by planning, sourcing, making and delivering their brands to customers.

Engineering graduates will be facing the challenges of large-scale production and given the accountability for making key decisions with the freedom to pioneer innovative solutions.

To find out more about Cadbury's graduate careers – or industrial placement opportunities – visit www.cadburygraduates.co.uk

Cadbury

make it yours.

There's nothing off the peg about our graduate scheme. It's individual. It's personalised. It's made for you to make your own. Each year we select a handful of talented, enthusiastic graduates to join us. We choose people who are genuinely excited to become part of the UK's largest confectionery company; who are passionate about the idea of working on our big name brands. Right from the start, you'll roll up your sleeves and get involved with real work, real learning and a challenging experience that'll turn you into one of the future leaders of our business. You'll succeed because you've got the tenacity to stamp your personality all over our graduate programme. And the confidence to take responsibility from the moment you walk in the door. Whatever you're into, you'll find ours a stimulating, inspiring world. We love what we do. We think you will too.

www.cadburygraduates.co.uk

finance • supply chain • engineering • sales & marketing

CANCER RESEARCH UK

graduates.cancerresearchuk.org

Vacancies for around 100+ graduates in 2010

- Accountancy
- Consulting
- Finance
- General Management
- Human Resources
- IT
- Marketing
- Purchasing
- Research & Development
- Retailing

Starting salary for 2010
£Competitive

Universities that Cancer Research UK plans to visit in 2009-10
Cambridge, Durham, Leeds, London, Oxford, Warwick
Please check with your university careers service for details of events.

Application deadline
See website for full details.

Contact Details
✉ graduate@cancer.org.uk
Turn to page 224 now to request more information or visit our new website at www.top100graduateemployers.com

Cancer Research UK is the world's leading independent organisation dedicated to cancer research. Their vision is that 'Together we will beat cancer' and their people have a passion, energy and commitment to achieving this ambitious agenda.

With an annual income of over £400 million Cancer Research UK combines pioneering research, business expertise and marketing talent: making it a world class centre of scientific excellence and the largest fundraising charity in the UK.

Clearly, a career with Cancer Research UK offers plenty in the way of personal fulfilment. But it's also a considerable challenge, calling for excellent communication skills, strategic thinking, innovation, and a determination to pursue fresh possibilities. Every year, Cancer Research UK offers a variety of graduate opportunities in all aspects of their work, including fundraising, marketing, science and corporate support services.

Few organisations can offer such a range of opportunities or allow graduates to make a real contribution. Cancer Research UK offers graduate training programmes, PhD Studentships, Internships and a variety of voluntary opportunities. To help successful applicants achieve their own ambitions, they will benefit from a unique combination of on-the-job learning and formal, professional training.

Cancer Research UK offers outstanding graduates the opportunity to work towards an outstanding goal.

To find out more about specific opportunities, visit their website graduates.cancerresearchuk.org

Beating cancer together sets our graduates apart.

Every graduate leaves university with dreams of making a difference. And yet few do it in a more meaningful way than improving their bank balance or a company's profit margin. It's a different story here at Cancer Research UK. From the moment our graduates join, they work together across every imaginable discipline to create scientific, commercial and creative innovations that have the potential to save lives. With such an important and challenging goal we need talented graduates who can bring fresh insights, excellent communication skills and a drive to succeed. If that sounds like you there's no better place to start your career. What sets you apart? Visit graduates.cancerresearchuk.org

Together we will beat cancer

CANCER RESEARCH UK

Vacancies for around 250 graduates in 2010

- Finance
- Human Resources
- Investment Banking
- IT

Vacancies also available in Europe, the USA, Asia and elsewhere in the world.

Starting salary for 2010
£Competitive

Universities that Citi plans to visit in 2009-10

Bath, Belfast, Bristol, Cambridge, Edinburgh, Glasgow, London, Manchester, Oxford, Reading, St Andrews, Ulster, Warwick

Please check with your university careers service for details of events.

Application deadline
8th November 2009

Contact Details

Turn to page 224 now to request more information or visit our new website at www.top100graduateemployers.com

Dreams. Realities.

Over the past twelve months the banking industry has experienced a period of significant change resulting in industry consolidation and calls for regulatory reforms. With this as a backdrop some may question why now is a great time to enter the industry. The answer is simple; banking and finance will always be a competitive, challenging and interesting career that requires the best talent to help drive forward positive change.

Citi is taking a lead role in helping the world's top corporations, governments and institutions adapt and be ready to flourish as financial markets return. Citi provides the best and brightest individuals an opportunity to make a difference at the most global bank in the world.

Citi's leadership has defined a new and clear vision for its future. A vision that is built on the foundation of what the firm has historically excelled at; providing the products and services that clients demand to more places around the world than anyone else. Citi is an institution founded on nearly 200 years of experience with operations in 140 countries. No other organisation can provide the range of financial services with which Citi serves its clients.

With its strategic direction, financial stability and global presence, Citi is a lead player and a great place to start a career. Full Time and Internship opportunities exist across a broad set of businesses including Investment Banking, Capital Markets Origination, Sales & Trading, Global Transaction Services, Risk, Technology, Operations and Human Resources.

Whatever path is chosen to take into the firm, Citi invests heavily in long term career education and tailored development programmes to help its people succeed.

OPPORTUNITY
NEVER SLEEPS.

Dreams.   Realities.

In Paris, after a hard day studying, Jen's finally ready to rest. Six time zones away, in New York, Lisa - Jen's future mentor - is shaking hands on funding for an irrigation project in Western Africa. Meanwhile, half a world away, Investment Banking Associate Rajid is returning from a meeting with government officials in Kazakhstan.

At any moment, someone in our global firm is opening new markets. Someone's closing deals. Someone's gaining skills to pass on to the next generation. A career with us is full of variety and challenge. Because Jen isn't working for us yet, but we've already been working for her. That's why, at Citi, opportunity never sleeps.
oncampus.citi.com

Opportunities in: Investment Banking, Capital Markets Origination, Sales & Trading, Global Transaction Services, Citi Investment Research and Analysis, Risk, Human Resources, Operations & Technology

Citi never sleeps

www.civilservice.gov.uk/faststream

Vacancies for around
500 graduates in 2010

■ Engineering
■ General Management
▨ Human Resources
■ IT

Starting salary for 2010
Up to £27,000

**Universities that the
Fast Stream
plans to visit in 2009-10**
Belfast, Birmingham,
Bristol, Brunel, Cardiff, City,
Edinburgh, Leeds, London,
Loughborough, Manchester,
Reading, Sheffield, Warwick
Please check with your university
careers service for details of events.

Application deadline
30th November 2009

Contact Details
✉ faststream@parity.net
☎ 01276 400333
Turn to page 224 now to request more
information or visit our new website at
www.top100graduateemployers.com

The Civil Service's accelerated graduate development programme

Education. Health. Employment. Defence. Transport. Climate change. International development. These are just some of the areas where graduates on the Civil Service Fast Stream get to put their ideas into practice, as they work on issues that affect the entire country and beyond.

The Civil Service Fast Stream is an accelerated graduate development programme aimed at people who have the potential to become the Civil Service leaders of tomorrow. As such, Fast Streamers are given considerable responsibility from the outset, challenged, and are moved regularly between postings to gain a wide range of experiences and skills.

They are exposed to three distinct but complementary professional areas: policy delivery, operational delivery and corporate services. These areas give them a wide understanding of how government delivers public services. As part of their development, graduates also enjoy a mixture of on-the-job training and formal courses, as well as receiving ongoing feedback on their performance.

So what qualities are needed to make it to the top? Lucidity, confidence, innovation and decisiveness are all important, as is an analytical and open-minded approach. Graduates must have a minimum 2:2 in any discipline.

Above all, they need to be able to develop relationships and deliver results, and be excited by the idea of making a real and positive impact across many different areas of society.

Other opportunities include specialist schemes for economists, statisticians, technology in business and HR.

For other Civil Service opportunities, visit www.civilservice.gov.uk/jobs

where will your IDEAS end up?

Our graduates don't just think about the big issues. They come up with innovative solutions and apply them to the real world. Employment? The economy? Climate change? Just some of the areas you could have an impact on as part of the Civil Service Fast Stream Graduate Programme. Find out more at www.civilservice.gov.uk/faststream

CIVILSERVICE
FASTSTREAM

CLIFFORD CHANCE

www.cliffordchance.com/gradsuk

Vacancies for around 100 graduates in 2010
For training contracts starting in 2012

Law

Starting salary for 2010
£37,400

Universities that Clifford Chance plans to visit in 2009-10
Aberdeen, Birmingham, Bristol, Cambridge, Durham, Edinburgh, Exeter, Glasgow, Leeds, Leicester, London, Manchester, Newcastle, Nottingham, Oxford, Southampton, St Andrews, Warwick, York
Please check with your university careers service for details of events.

Application deadline
Law: 31st July 2010
Non-Law: 31st January 2010

Contact Details
✉ Recruitment.London@ cliffordchance.com
☎ 020 7006 3003
Turn to page 224 now to request more information or visit our new website at www.top100graduateemployers.com

Clifford Chance is a leading international law firm delivering innovative and practical legal solutions to corporate, institutional, and government clients around the world. The firm's rapid expansion through a series of groundbreaking mergers has fostered a culture that is both pioneering and entrepreneurial, flexible and open. The culture emphasises the fundamental importance of teamwork and of providing dynamic career opportunities for its people.

Clifford Chance's international network of offices, provides clients with local expertise in all major markets and offers trainees and lawyers unmatched opportunities for international exposure, as well as the very real prospect of secondments to overseas offices and to major client organisations.

The firm's scale and reach across six global practices – Corporate, Capital Markets, Banking and Finance, Real Estate, Litigation and Dispute Resolution, and Tax, Pensions and Employment – each features many different teams that work together and share a deep understanding of their clients and the sectors they work in. Working within these teams will constitute the main part of training and will provide the foundations for the trainee's future career.

Trainees at Clifford Chance can look forward to learning about business and law in a diverse and supportive environment, with exposure to deals and clients that populate the business headlines. In addition, the firm's commitment to an extensive range of pro bono and community projects further adds to the breadth of opportunity, enabling lawyers to use their skills and business experience and develop truly rewarding legal careers.

it's WE not ME

For you, as a trainee or a vacation scheme student, it is the culture, the atmosphere and the people you work alongside that will shape the quality of your experience and, ultimately, your future career. Find out about opportunities at Clifford Chance, an international law firm built on collaboration, innovation and a relentless commitment to quality in everything we do.

From different backgrounds, countries and cultures, we work together. Together we are Clifford Chance.

www.cliffordchance.com/gradsuk

We have a global commitment to diversity, dignity and inclusiveness.

Clifford Chance LLP

CLIFFORD CHANCE

FT FINANCIAL TIMES

Winner Innovative Lawyers Awards 2008

The **co-operative**

www.co-operative.jobs/graduates

Vacancies for around 20 graduates in 2010

■ Finance

■ General Management

The **co-operative**
From community projects to a share of the profits, renewable energy to Fairtrade products, we believe that when the benefits are passed around, it's **good for everyone**

Starting salary for 2010
£Competitive

Universities that The Co-operative Group plans to visit in 2009-10
Cambridge, Lancaster, Leeds, Liverpool, Manchester, Oxford, Sheffield, Warwick
Please check with your university careers service for details of events.

Application deadline
See website for full details.

Contact Details
✉ graduate.recruitment@ co-op.co.uk

Turn to page 224 now to request more information or visit our new website at www.top100graduateemployers.com

With 16 different businesses, 4,900 outlets and 110,000 people, The Co-operative Group isn't just a food retailer but also a travel provider, a funeral director, a pharmacist, a legal services provider, and much more.

But the real difference lies not just in what they do; it's what they are – a co-operative (and the world's largest consumer co-operative at that). Unlike a plc, they do not just exist to make profit. Everything they do is for the benefit of their members and the community as a whole. They are driven by their social goals and their co-operative values give them a positive advantage.

But that doesn't mean they are any less ambitious – they still offer the depth and breadth of challenge expected from a commercially focussed business. For those who want to pursue a rewarding career without compromising their values, the Group offers two programmes: Business Management and Finance.

On the Business Management programme, whether it be Funeralcare, marketing or Food Retail operations, graduates can choose from a wide range of business critical projects ensuring the entire experience meets their career aspirations. On the other hand, graduates with a passion for finance might want to consider the CIMA accredited programme. This gives them transactional experience of accounting software packages and an overview of financial processes. It will sharpen their commercial approach through working directly with the different businesses, as well as giving them a broad perspective of financial strategy.

Whichever route they choose, graduates will gain experience across the businesses and develop technical knowledge and professional skills through The Co-operative Group's structured development programme.

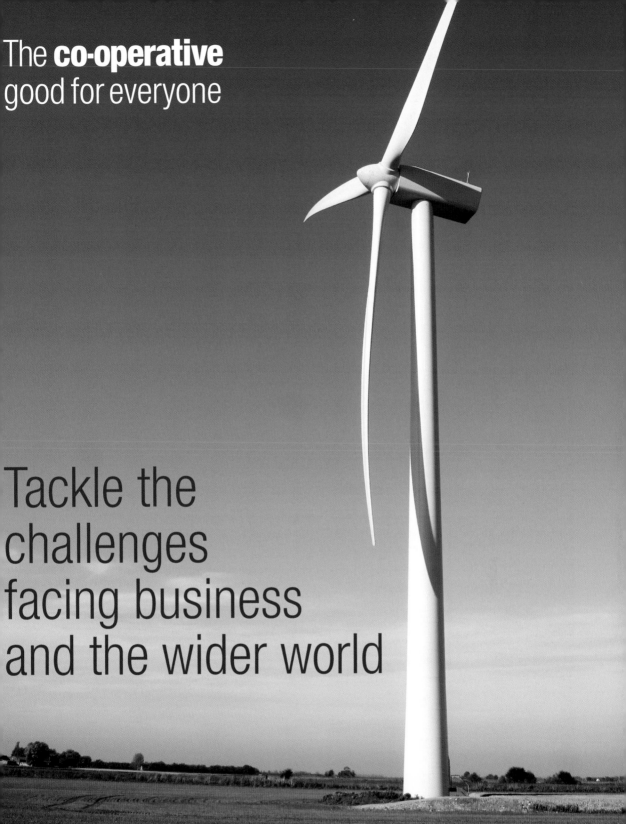

Vacancies for around TBC graduates in 2010

- Engineering
- Finance
- Human Resources
- Logistics
- Manufacturing
- Purchasing
- Research & Development

Starting salary for 2010
£Competitive

Universities that Corus plans to visit in 2009-10
Aston, Bath, Birmingham, Bristol, Cambridge, Cardiff, London, Loughborough, Manchester, Nottingham, Oxford, Sheffield, Southampton, Warwick
Please check with your university careers service for details of events.

Application deadline
Year-round recruitment

Contact Details
✉ recruitment@corusgroup.com
☎ 01926 488025

Turn to page 224 now to request more information or visit our new website at www.top100graduateemployers.com

Imagine what the world would be like without steel. No hospitals, schools, transportation systems, even paperclips; the list is endless! Corus is now part of Tata Steel, one of the world's largest steel producers, with a combined presence in nearly 50 countries.

Corus metal is used globally in projects such as the Bugatti Veyron, the Delhi Metro and the Petronas Towers. Closer to home it is used for the new Wembley Stadium, track for the London underground and the London Eye.

Corus is passionate about making the world a better place and is committed to the adoption of sustainable practices. Using the perfect blend of world-class manufacturing processes, innovative research centres and inspired individuals; Corus can achieve the vision of becoming leaders in their field.

To achieve this vision, people with qualities that will fit into the Corus way of thinking are essential; these include passion, drive, enthusiasm, imagination and the ability to adapt to new challenges. Corus look for innovative minds and skills that go beyond just pure academic ability in order to drive change and really make a difference.

Corus has the size and diversity to tailor careers by providing real life projects from the outset and challenges that will be interesting, dynamic and relevant to the business. Those entering the company receive on the job and formal training (including Professional Accreditation) designed to develop management and technical skills.

corus

1D
Blast Furnace No. 5

produces	liquid iron
temperature	1,500°C
iron output	2,500,000t/year
cost	£75m
carbon content	4%
steel expertise	Corus

2F
Expert development

world-class

3A
Bugatti Veyron

mph	
hp	
cc	254
cylinders	987
weight	7,993
steel expertise	16
	1.9t
	Corus

From raw product to best in class

A future in steel

We are passionate about making the world a better place. Using the perfect blend of world-class manufacturing processes, innovative research centres and inspired individuals, we can achieve the vision of becoming leaders in our field.

Iconic projects such as the Bugatti Veyron, Wembley Stadium and the Petronas Towers include our steel expertise and development.

To find out more about the opportunities within Corus visit our website.

www.corusgroupcareers.com

TATA
TATA STEEL

Corus is part of Tata Steel

CREDIT SUISSE

www.credit-suisse.com/careers

Vacancies for around
150-250 **graduates in 2010**

- Finance
- Investment Banking
- IT

Starting salary for 2010
£Competitive

Universities Credit Suisse plans to visit in 2009-10
Cambridge, City,
London, Manchester,
Oxford, Warwick
Please check with your university
careers service for details of events.

Application deadline
20th November 2009

Contact Details
Turn to page 224 now to request more
information or visit our new website at
www.top100graduateemployers.com

Credit Suisse provides private banking, investment banking and asset management services to clients across the world. Active in over 50 countries and employing more than 46,000 people, Credit Suisse is one of the world's premier banks.

They offer intellectual challenges, high rewards and global development potential for individuals who share an enthusiasm for partnering clients to achieve business success. There are opportunities in investment banking (including fixed income and equities), asset management, information technology, operations and other support functions, as well as a range of internships and placement schemes.

Credit Suisse's training programs are designed to be best in class. Content varies among business areas, but all programs combine formal learning with on-the-job practice and personal coaching to create an environment for further development. And, their award-winning Business School encourages ongoing learning and growth.

It's not easy choosing the right career – or the right place to start that career – but from spending a little time exploring, the decision gets easier. Most people who join Credit Suisse do so because of 'the people'. Credit Suisse appeals to intelligent and outgoing personalities who want to work together in an atmosphere of co-operation and respect. It's a different perspective on how a big bank should go about its business, but it works for Credit Suisse.

They need individuals who bring something personal, special and unique to the business. It's not just that different jobs call for different skills and aptitudes; the creativity, flair and agility that make Credit Suisse successful flow directly from the special mix of people who work there.

Some think one point of view.

We think thousands of opinions.

There's great strength in keeping an open mind. A great wisdom to be had from sharing personal experience. We trust our people to work together to drive our business forward. And this is one of many reasons that we remain strong, despite the challenges of today's markets.

Take a closer look at **www.credit-suisse.com/careers**

Thinking New Perspectives.

CREDIT SUISSE

Deloitte.

www.deloitte.co.uk/graduates

Vacancies for around 1,000 graduates in 2010

- Accountancy
- Consulting
- Finance
- IT

Starting salary for 2010
£Competitive

Universities that Deloitte plans to visit in 2009-10
Please check with your university careers service for details of events.

Application deadline
Year-round recruitment

Contact Details
Turn to page 224 now to request more information or visit our new website at www.top100graduateemployers.com

How do you feel about your future?
You should feel nothing but excitement

Deloitte's breadth and depth of service means they can offer graduates a wide range of career opportunities. Providing fully integrated advice across Audit, Tax, Consulting and Corporate Finance, Deloitte is a leading force in the professional services industry, with 150,000 people across the globe and 11,000 in the UK alone.

Working across all major industries, from Financial Services, Technology, Media & Telecommunications, through to Consumer Business and Travel & Tourism, Deloitte offers the kind of clients, complexity and challenges graduates need to continue their personal growth.

The professional services Deloitte provides are absolutely vital to their clients' businesses. The way they work is uniquely collaborative: by drawing on expertise from across the firm, Deloitte creates integrated teams to meet the full range of challenges their clients face.

The training and development programmes Deloitte provides are second to none. They nurture talent with programmes that are tailor-made for each individual. From the Summer Vacation Scheme to their Insight Days, there are many ways to find out what working with Deloitte is really like, even before graduation.

Deloitte believes in plain speaking, pragmatic thinking, delivering on their promises, and a good work-life balance. And whatever degree has been achieved, successful applicants will be working with the best in every field. All of which makes Deloitte's offices very special places to work.

What does our sponsorship of the London 2012 Games mean to you?

The chance to be inspired, achieve and deliver

Graduate vacancies

As official supporters, we are playing an important role in helping deliver a successful London 2012 Olympic and Paralympic Games. Join us and our strong association with London 2012 means you'll feel great pride in your firm. We also hope our support of the athletes captures your imagination and inspires you to achieve great things – in your career and with clients. Plus you could be one of the hundreds of our people who will work directly with the London 2012 Organising Committee – so that when the time comes, you'll be able to watch the Games knowing you helped make them happen. It's your future. How far will you take it?

official professional services provider
to the Olympic and Paralympic Games

Deloitte.

Discover more at
www.deloitte.co.uk/graduates

DLA PIPER

**Vacancies for around
85 graduates in 2010**
For training contracts starting in 2012

 Law

Starting salary for 2010
£Competitive

**Universities DLA Piper
plans to visit in 2009-10**
Aberdeen, Birmingham,
Bristol, Cambridge,
Cardiff, Dundee, Durham,
Edinburgh, Exeter, Glasgow,
Kent, Lancaster, Leeds,
Leicester, Liverpool,
London, Manchester,
Newcastle, Nottingham,
Oxford, Sheffield,
Strathclyde, Warwick, York
Please check with your university
careers service for details of events.

Application deadline
31st July 2010

Contact Details
✉ recruitment.graduate@
dlapiper.com
Turn to page 224 now to request more
information or visit our new website at
www.top100graduateemployers.com

DLA Piper is one of the world's largest law firms. With more
than 3,700 lawyers across 29 countries throughout Asia,
Europe, the Middle East and the US, DLA Piper is positioned to
help companies with their legal needs anywhere in the world.

Their current vision is to be the leading global business law firm.
Clients include some of the world's leading businesses, governments,
banks and financial institutions. DLA Piper offers trainees in all UK offices
the opportunity to apply for a range of client and international secondments.

In 2008 DLA Piper won the prestigious National Graduate Recruitment
Awards' 'Diversity Recruitment Award', proving their commitment to recruiting
people from a wide variety of backgrounds and ages.

There is no 'standard' DLA Piper trainee, however they do require a strong
academic background and look for good communicators and team players.
As well as this, in line with the firm's main focus of work, a keen interest in
the corporate world is essential – as is an appetite for life!

Trainees complete four six-month seats and progress is monitored through
regular reviews and feedback. The in-house Professional Skills Course
combined with high-quality on-the-job experience means an excellent
grounding on which DLA Piper's trainees build their professional careers.

The firm operates a formal summer scheme, which runs between June
and August each year. The schemes run for two weeks and allow a
thorough insight into DLA Piper. There are approximately 170 places
available nationwide.

SQUEEZE MORE INTO TWO YEARS
WE OFFER YOU ONE OF THE SHARPEST
TRAINING CONTRACTS AROUND

Everything matters and every day counts when you're a trainee at DLA Piper. We squeeze huge amounts of experience, responsibility and personal development into your 24 months with us. That means you get to know more about the law, our firm and about yourself.

Working with one of the world's leading practices also means more opportunities: the chance to try the things you want to try, work on secondments abroad or with clients, and get involved with headline making matters.

Enjoy every last bit of your training contract and develop the all round skills that all top lawyers need. Visit our website for more details: www.dlapiper.com

[dstl]

www.dstl.gov.uk/careers

Vacancies for around 150 graduates in 2010

- Engineering
- IT
- Research & Development

Starting salary for 2010
£22,000

Universities that Dstl plans to visit in 2009-10

Bath, Birmingham, Cambridge, Cardiff, Durham, Edinburgh, Exeter, Heriot-Watt, Lancaster, Leicester, London, Loughborough, Manchester, Newcastle, Nottingham, Oxford, Plymouth, Sheffield, Southampton, St Andrews, Strathclyde, Surrey, Warwick, York
Please check with your university careers service for details of events.

Application deadline
Year-round recruitment

Contact Details

✉ graduates@dstl.gov.uk

☎ 01980 613755

Turn to page 224 now to request more information or visit our new website at www.top100graduateemployers.com

Dstl's work matters – saving lives – both on the battlefield and on the home front.

Working at Dstl (Defence Science and Technology Laboratory) can be very exciting from blowing things up and large-scale virtual wargames, to helping to design jet fighter ejector seats and working with underwater remote-controlled robots. Some Dstl staff go to the frontline to give critical scientific advice to senior military commanders and some are on call round-the-clock to deal with any chemical or biological threat in the UK.

Dstl provides science and engineering-based products, services and expertise to the government on defence and science issues and its mission is to create the winning edge for UK armed forces through the best use of science and technology.

Dstl tackles and solves some of the most challenging science and technology problems facing the government, armed forces and security services – wherever and whenever they arise.

Careers at Dstl cover applied sciences, biological and health sciences, physical sciences and engineering, through to project management and finance.

Dstl offers a range of rewards and benefits to help graduates progress their careers and there is a strong emphasis on continued personal development with ongoing relevant training. Dstl encourages its employees to make the most of their potential from achieving professional chartered status and sponsorship for further relevant qualifications to offering secondments and mentors. There are also flexible working hours so people can fit a career around their lifestyle.

And it may seem a bit early to be thinking about it ... but Dstl benefits include a choice of valuable pension arrangements.

For Science.
For Technology.
For Defence.
This is where it begins.

Dstl is a vital agency of the Ministry of Defence. We tackle some of the world's most challenging science and technology issues head on. Our innovation and advice pushes boundaries to solve problems for the UK Government, Armed Forces and Security Services. It's work that takes us from the front line to the bottom of the ocean, making the impossible possible, saving lives.

Every year we hire UK graduates from a wide range of backgrounds. If you've a strong academic record you could be one of them. The training and development opportunities you'll receive ensure you build a thriving career, while enjoying real balance in your life. And you'll make use of the capabilities you've already developed on work that is demanding, exciting, rewarding. Work that is essential to national security. Work that matters.

Due to the nature of our work, these roles are only available to UK nationals and are subject to security clearance.

www.dstl.gov.uk/careers

[dstl]

e·on

www.eon-uk.com/graduates

Vacancies for around
35 graduates in 2010

- Engineering
- Finance
- General Management
- Human Resources
- IT
- Marketing
- Sales

Vacancies also available in Europe.

Starting salary for 2010
£25,066

Universities that E.ON plans to visit in 2009-10
Aberdeen, Aston,
Bath, Birmingham, Bristol,
Cardiff, Durham,
Leeds, Leicester,
Liverpool, London,
Loughborough, Manchester,
Newcastle, Nottingham,
Nottingham Trent,
Sheffield, Warwick
Please check with your university
careers service for details of events.

Application deadline
22nd December 2009

Contact Details
✉ gradrecruitment@eon-uk.com
Turn to page 224 now to request more
information or visit our new website at
www.top100graduateemployers.com

As one of the world's largest energy companies the decisions that E.ON makes matter. Finding a way to produce clean, reliable and affordable energy, whilst building a future infrastructure the world can be proud of are some of the challenges E.ON faces and takes seriously. By joining E.ON, graduates can play a leading role in solving them.

E.ON's graduate programmes in Engineering, General Management, Finance, Human Resources, Sales and Marketing, and IT are designed to truly stretch and challenge. They'll expose graduates to all areas of E.ON's international business and give them lots of responsibility. In return for dedication, courage and initiative successful applicants will be rewarded with a great starting salary, lots of benefits, personal development (including the opportunity to gain professional qualifications), and even the chance to build an international career.

Successful graduates can make a huge impact. This is their chance to take action – by joining the energy debate and helping shape the future. E.ON is one of the world's largest investor owned energy companies, and is using its size and resources to tackle climate change head-on. Already one of the world's leading green generators, E.ON is investing billions in developing a diverse generation portfolio over the coming years, developing the latest technologies to reduce carbon emissions and improve energy efficiency.

So, from tackling large scale projects, to gaining professional qualifications, all those who demonstrate passion, commitment and drive will have the chance to become E.ON's future technical or business leaders – making a positive impact on people's lives and the environment.

"I'm just one person, what difference can I make?"

It's by working together that we get things done, surpass expectations and push boundaries. Just ask our graduates. Working with mentors, each other and the rest of our business, they're gaining the skills and professional qualifications they need to tackle the energy industry's greatest challenges head-on. Like how we'll go about meeting tomorrow's energy demands in a sustainable way. Or how changes in technology will affect the way we do everything – from growing our team to selling our products at an affordable price. These aren't just questions for engineers. Whatever your discipline, you could find your place here, and make your mark on the energy landscape.

"All the difference when you're part of the team"

eon-uk.com/graduates

www.edfenergy.com/TT100

Vacancies for around 112 graduates in 2010

- Engineering
- Finance
- General Management
- Human Resources
- IT

Vacancies also available in Europe.

Starting salary for 2010
£22,500-£26,000

Universities EDF Energy plans to visit in 2009-10

Bath, Belfast, Birmingham, Bristol, Cambridge, Cardiff, Edinburgh, Exeter, Glasgow, Heriot-Watt, Lancaster, Leeds, Liverpool, London, Manchester, Nottingham, Oxford, Plymouth, Sheffield, Southampton, St Andrews, Strathclyde, Surrey, Warwick, York
Please check with your university careers service for details of events.

Application deadline
December 2009

Contact Details
✉ graduateenquiries@edfenergy.com
Turn to page 224 now to request more information or visit our new website at www.top100graduateemployers.com

In the coming years, the energy industry will face some of the greatest challenges in its history. Fluctuating oil prices, fierce competition, the need for investment, the growing challenge posed by climate change – all of these will play a part.

EDF Energy is perfectly placed to tackle these issues – because it is growing too. Recently, EDF Energy joined forces with British Energy – the largest generator of electricity in the UK, and a major player in nuclear power.

The integration of the two companies makes EDF Energy a unique proposition. They now boast expertise in a wide range of energy sources – and across every stage of the energy process: generation, trading, distribution and supply. They're championing sustainability through partnerships with the Mayor of London and the London 2012 Games. They're also involved in major projects – from airports to business districts. In fact, with British Energy now on board, they're likely to be directly involved with the major developments of the industry for many years to come.

The same can be said for their graduates: the schemes are designed to support, test and develop people who have the potential to be future industry leaders. As one might expect from such an extraordinarily diverse organisation, there are a number of areas graduates can explore. There are opportunities in nuclear, civil, electrical, mechanical and chemical engineering; physics, chemistry and mathematics; and a wide range of business areas – from finance and commercial to IT, HR and analysis.

It takes many brilliant minds to tackle the world's energy challenges.

Thankfully we've just acquired thousands more.

www.edfenergy.com/TT100

Save Today Save Tomorrow

Environment Agency

Vacancies for around 10-20 graduates in 2010

Engineering

Starting salary for 2010
£22,000-£24,000

Universities that the Environment Agency plans to visit in 2009-10
Please check with your university careers service for details of events.

Application deadline
See website for full details.

Contact Details
✉ gradengineers@environment-agency.gov.uk
☎ 0845 601 2233

Turn to page 224 now to request more information or visit our new website at www.top100graduateemployers.com

Flooding is one of the most important issues facing humankind. Right now, five million people, over two million homes and businesses are at risk of flooding in England. This threat is only going to get worse with climate change.

But graduates can help do something about it. The Environment Agency is responsible for protecting and improving the environment in England and Wales, spending over £800 million every year on a breathtaking range of flood and coastal erosion risk management projects. That's well over half the budget – the rest goes towards other crucial work, such as acting as regulators on waste disposal and nuclear safety, addressing the impact of pollution, influencing government policy, managing conservation work and leading awareness campaigns to raise the profile of important environmental issues.

As a graduate, this is a chance to join the Environment Agency's team of engineers, many of them world leaders in their field, and face the threat head on. They are involved in a number of activities, including providing a unique emergency response service that minimises the risk of flooding in rapidly changing weather conditions; building and maintaining flood defences; creating protective wetlands; raising awareness amongst those at risk; and influencing the way government, local authorities and house builders develop land.

While following the Graduate Training Scheme, graduates will undertake a variety of diverse projects around the business that will help them become leading engineers in their own right. The Environment Agency also wants to help the flood and coastal erosion risk engineers of tomorrow, today. People who are studying towards an accredited BEng and will be progressing to MEng (or equivalent) can apply for a sponsorship opportunity.

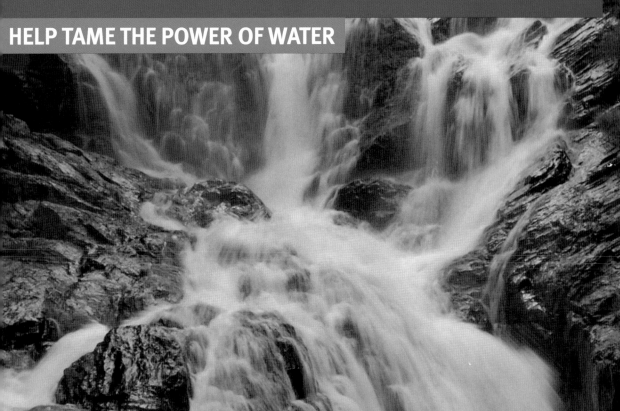

Environment Agency

CIVIL ENGINEERS

HELP TAME THE POWER OF WATER

MEng/BEng/Sponsorship Opportunities

Water is astonishing. It can power homes, of course, but it can also sweep them away. We already work to maintain 36,000 kilometres of river and coastline defences, but the threat of erosion and flooding continues to grow. That's why we're constantly planning, developing and testing new, ever-more innovative defences, and our Civil Engineers are crucial if we're to succeed. They are there from start to finish; their superb technical skills are matched only by their ability to work with the community. Their work helps to save lives and livelihoods. Is there anywhere more important you could take your career? Find out about our graduate and sponsorship opportunities by visiting
www.environment-agency.gov.uk/jobs

CIVIL ENGINEERING WITH MORE IMPACT

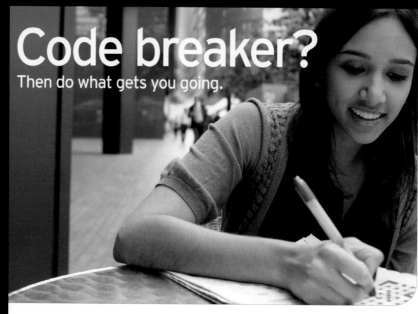

What gets you going?

Wherever you want to work, you'll have a more enjoyable and successful time if you do what you're best at.

The trick is to work with your strengths. It's what we do at Ernst & Young and how we make sure our people and our clients achieve their potential. The first step is to discover what your strengths are.

So visit www.ey.com/uk/careers to learn more about us and the kind of role that's right for you.

We actively support the Borneo Team Challenge - just one way in which Ernst & Young people are helping The Prince's Trust.

ⵏⵏ ERNST & YOUNG
Quality In Everything We Do

INVESTOR IN PEOPLE

ExxonMobil

Vacancies for around 60 graduates in 2010

- Engineering
- Finance
- Human Resources
- IT
- Marketing
- Retailing
- Sales

Vacancies also available elsewhere in the world.

Starting salary for 2010
£33,000+

Universities ExxonMobil plans to visit in 2009-10

Aberdeen, Aston, Bath, Belfast, Birmingham, Cambridge, Edinburgh, Heriot-Watt, London, Loughborough, Manchester, Newcastle, Nottingham, Southampton, Strathclyde, Surrey
Please check with your university careers service for details of events.

Application deadline
Year-round recruitment

Contact Details

✉ uk.vacancies@exxonmobil.com

Turn to page 224 now to request more information or visit our new website at www.top100graduateemployers.com

Exxon Mobil Corporation is an industry leader in almost every aspect of the energy and petrochemical business. They operate facilities or market products in most of the world's countries and explore for oil and natural gas on six continents.

Exxon Mobil Corporation is the parent company of the Esso, Mobil and ExxonMobil companies that operate in the UK. They operate in a sector that is dynamic, strategically important and exciting. Their customers are both global and local, ranging from major airlines to the million customers a day who visit their UK service stations.

A broad range of exciting career opportunities are available within both commercial and technical functions, where graduates can expect immediate responsibility. Job rotations offer graduates the opportunity to test and develop their skills, applying them to new and exciting challenges.

ExxonMobil offer various development programmes, aimed at equipping graduates with the skills required to become leaders of the future. One of the programmes which many of their graduates attend is the ExxonMobil Graduate Development Programme, run in conjunction with the internationally renowned London Business School (LBS).

This is a two year, modular course covering business awareness, interpersonal skills and people management, leading to alumni status with the LBS upon completion of the programme. Obtaining Chartership status is also encouraged where appropriate, e.g. IChemE and CIMA.

Rapid skills growth and career development is standard and graduates can expect a high degree of intellectual challenge and change.

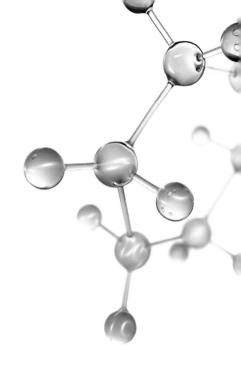

by 2030, global energy demand will increase by about 30%.

It's a **challenge** like no other.
And it will be solved by someone like **you**.

Aviation
Engineering Specialist
Finance
Geoscience
Human Resources
Information Technology
Sales & Marketing
Production
Refining & Chemicals
One year internships
Summer internships

The need for energy is a very real economic issue. It affects literally everyone – everywhere in the world. At ExxonMobil, we're uniquely positioned to help find the answers to the world's toughest energy challenges. We have the resources, the technology, and the commitment of people just like you.

When you build your career here, you have the opportunity to make a profound impact. From inventing new technologies, to unlocking new sources of petroleum, to developing more efficient fuel and engine systems, you can make the breakthroughs happen.

The biggest challenges attract the best. Whether your background is in business, engineering or science, ExxonMobil has a challenging career waiting for you.

exxonmobil.com/ukrecruitment

Esso **Mobil**

Brands of **ExxonMobil**

Taking on the world's toughest energy challenges.™

Vacancies for around 106 graduates in 2010

- Accountancy
- Consulting
- Finance
- Human Resources
- Investment Banking

Starting salary for 2010
£29,000
Plus a £2,500 joining bonus, as well as further performance-related rewards.

Universities that the Financial Services Authority plans to visit in 2009-10
Please check with your university careers service for details of events.

Application deadline
9th November 2009

Contact Details
✉ fsa.graduates@fsa.gov.uk

Turn to page 224 now to request more information or visit our new website at www.top100graduateemployers.com

The Financial Services Authority is the UK's sole financial services regulator. Its remit covers four key areas: to maintain market confidence; to raise public awareness of the financial system; to ensure consumers are protected and to target and reduce financial crime.

In today's financial climate, a robust regulatory stance is crucial. So whether its working with banks, building societies and insurance companies or financial advisers, fund managers, mortgage brokers or intermediaries, the FSA applies the same firm but fair standards.

Opportunities exist for people with the potential to develop and the talent to deliver. The FSA's graduate programmes are carefully constructed to give graduates real responsibility and valuable experience from day one. As well as the generalist programme, there are specialist law, HR, actuarial, economics and management accounting programmes.

Following a comprehensive induction, successful applicants will be allocated two placements that will give them in-depth exposure to FSA work. Later, they'll have their third and final rotation which includes a six-month external secondment will enable them to view the industry from a different perspective.

The starting salary for graduates is £29,000 – plus also a £2,500 joining bonus, as well as further performance-related rewards and an array of excellent benefits.

In addition to a 2.1 in any subject, 300 UCAS tariff points and the unrestricted right to work in the UK, graduates will need to be decisive, results-driven, highly analytical team players with excellent people skills and initiative. For more information and to apply go to www.fsagraduates.com

FRESHFIELDS BRUCKHAUS DERINGER

www.freshfields.com/uktrainees

Vacancies for around 90 graduates in 2010

For training contracts starting in 2012

 Law

Starting salary for 2010
£39,000

Universities Freshfields Bruckhaus Deringer plans to visit in 2009-10

Birmingham, Bristol, Cambridge, Durham, Kent, Leeds, London, Manchester, Nottingham, Oxford, Sheffield, Southampton, Warwick, York

Please check with your university careers service for details of events.

Application deadline
31st July 2010

Contact Details

✉ uktrainees@freshfields.com

☎ 020 7785 5554

Turn to page 224 now to request more information or visit our new website at www.top100graduateemployers.com

Freshfields is a leader among international law firms. With over 2,700 lawyers in 27 key business centres around the world, the firm provides a comprehensive service to national and multinational corporations, financial institutions and governments.

Trainee solicitors receive a thorough professional training in a very broad range of practice areas, an excellent personal development programme and the chance to work in one of the firm's international offices or on secondment with a client. Successful applicants will be working with and learning from one of the most talented peer groups in the legal world, and will get the blend of support and freedom they need to evolve their career and take advantage of the opportunities the firm's international network offers. Flexibility is one of the hallmarks of the training programme and one of the features which most differentiates Freshfields' training contract from others.

The firm has a friendly and relaxed atmosphere which comes from having a diverse range of individuals who share a strong set of common values. It recognises the importance of ensuring that people are able to keep their lives in balance, and therefore encourages a range of sporting, cultural and social activities, as well as participation in their award-winning corporate social responsibility programme.

The firm is looking for those with proven academic ability, an excellent command of spoken and written English, high levels of drive and determination, good team-working skills and excellent organisational ability.

FRESHFIELDS BRUCKHAUS DERINGER

A collapsed building society, an Australian thoroughbred, 5,000 blood tests and an unmissable 2012 deadline.

EXPERIENCE LIFE AT FRESHFIELDS

We offer our trainees a breadth of training, opportunity and experience that few firms can match – so it's not surprising that many of our lawyers have amazing stories to tell.

This is due to the nature of our firm – truly international with over 2,600 lawyers in 27 key business centres around the world – and to the flexibility of our training programme. You can choose up to eight different seats, spend time in one of our overseas offices or go on secondment to one of our clients (and sometimes do both).

It's no wonder the people who work with us have such an eclectic range of experiences to look back on over their careers.

And as you'll be working with and learning from some of the most talented business lawyers in the world, you'll gain the experience and knowledge you need to become not just a world-class lawyer but a trusted business advisor too.

Find out more at:
www.freshfields.com/uktrainees

provider · provider · Paralympic Games

Vacancies for around 100+ graduates in 2010

- Engineering
- General Management
- IT
- Research & Development
- Other

Starting salary for 2010
£24,945

Universities that GCHQ plans to visit in 2009-10
Please check with your university careers service for details of events.

Application deadline
Varies by function
See website for full details.

Contact Details
✉ recruitment@gchq.gsi.gov.uk

Turn to page 224 now to request more information or visit our new website at www.top100graduateemployers.com

GCHQ is one of the UK's three intelligence services, alongside MI5 and MI6. The only one based outside London – in Cheltenham – it has two very specific roles in helping counter threats which compromise national and global security.

The first is to gather and analyse intelligence, using some of the world's most powerful technology, which helps shape Britain's response to global events. Teams of IT, electronics and telecommunications specialists manage the equipment, while mathematicians, linguists and intelligence analysts study and interpret the information it provides. This information is then used by customers – for example, the Government, law enforcement agencies and the military – to inform foreign policy or fight terrorism and crime.

The second is to provide technical advice for the protection of Government communication and information systems. This specialist work is the responsibility of CESG – The National Technical Authority for Information Assurance.

In both, the focus is on keeping one step ahead of people who are, in turn, trying to keep one step ahead of GCHQ. This means the work is constantly evolving, extremely challenging, and always interesting. GCHQ employs around 5,000 people – mainly in Cheltenham – and recruits graduates from various disciplines into entry level roles in a huge range of operational and support functions.

While the work is totally unique, the skills – and professional qualifications – graduates gain will be industry standard, and transferable. Everyone benefits from personalised training, mentoring and shadowing. Applicants must be British citizens.

Get under the skin of it

Graduate opportunities | Cheltenham | £24,945 + benefits

One of the UK's intelligence services, GCHQ's role is two-fold: to gather and analyse intelligence which helps shape Britain's response to global events, and, to provide technical advice for the protection of Government communication and information systems. In doing so, our specialists – in IT, internet, engineering, languages, information assurance, mathematics and intelligence – get well beneath the surface of global affairs. If you thought the world was an interesting place, you really ought to explore our world of work.

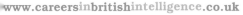

www.careersinbritishintelligence.co.uk

Applicants must be British citizens. GCHQ values diversity and welcomes applicants from all sections of the community. We want our workforce to reflect the diversity of our work.

it's an interesting world

GlaxoSmithKline

**Vacancies for around
40-50 graduates in 2010**

- Engineering
- Finance
- IT
- Manufacturing
- Marketing
- Purchasing
- Research & Development
- Sales

Starting salary for 2010
£Competitive

**Universities that
GlaxoSmithKline
plans to visit in 2009-10**
Please check with your university
careers service for details of events.

Application deadline
Year-round recruitment

Contact Details
Turn to page 224 now to request more
information or visit our new website at
www.top100graduateemployers.com

GlaxoSmithKline (GSK) is a place where ideas come to life.
As one of the world's leading research-based pharmaceutical
companies, GSK is dedicated to delivering products and
medicines that help millions of people around the world do
more, feel better and live longer.

Based in the UK, with operations in the US and over 100 countries worldwide,
GSK makes almost 4 billion packs of medicine and healthcare products every
year. And much of this is thanks to an extensive product range that includes
everything from prescription medicines and vaccines to popular consumer
healthcare products.

So while some people depend on GSK's pioneering pharmaceutical products
to tackle life-threatening illnesses, others choose best-selling nutritional brands
such as Lucozade and Ribena for a feel-good boost. GSK even manages to
brighten smiles with some of the world's favourite toothpaste brands.

But being a leader brings responsibility and means that GSK must also help
developing countries where debilitating disease affects millions of people.
To meet this challenge, GSK is committed to providing discounted medicines
where they are needed the most. GSK's new volunteering programme 'Pulse'
empowers employees to use their skills and knowledge to make a significant
difference in impoverished communities at home or abroad.

New starters at GSK soon see that there's no such thing as a typical career
path. With so much geographical and business diversity on offer, as well as a
number of industrial placements across all business functions, there are plenty
of opportunities to learn and develop. Find out more about the opportunities on
offer by visiting GSK at www.gsk.com/uk-students

ENGINEERING

SCIENCE

IT

SALES & MARKETING

FINANCE

PURCHASING

YOU'LL BE AMAZED HOW MUCH GOES INTO OUR PRODUCTS.

Graduate Opportunities: Sales, Marketing, Finance, Science, IT, Purchasing and Engineering

It's a fact that science is a vital part of what we do. Look beyond that though, and you'll see everything happening at GSK is a real team effort from beginning to end, where a variety of different specialist departments come together to achieve incredible results. And that means as one of the world's leading research-based pharmaceutical and healthcare companies, we're in a great position to offer a wide range of unmissable opportunities to graduates from any degree background.

Discover why our success depends on so much more than science. Visit **www.gsk.com/uk-students**

Together we can make life better.

gsk GlaxoSmithKline   gsk.com/uk-students

Goldman Sachs

gs.com/careers

Vacancies for around TBC graduates in 2010

- Finance
- Investment Banking
- IT

Starting salary for 2010
£Competitive

Universities that Goldman Sachs plans to visit in 2009-10
Please check with your university careers service for details of events.

Application deadline
18th October 2009

Contact Details
Turn to page 224 now to request more information or visit our new website at www.top100graduateemployers.com

Goldman Sachs is a global investment banking, securities and investment management firm. They provide a wide range of services to a substantial and diversified client base that includes corporations, financial institutions, governments, non-profit organisations and high net worth individuals.

Goldman Sachs' business is structured in a series of specialised divisions: Finance, Global Compliance, Global Investment Research, Legal & Management Controls, Investment Banking; Investment Management; Merchant Banking, Operations, Securities Division and Technology.

Goldman Sachs welcomes graduates from a wide range of university courses and backgrounds. There are a number of different stages when graduates can consider joining Goldman Sachs. Naturally, they will be given different degrees of exposure and responsibility but whether it is as an intern, a new analyst or a new associate, successful applicants will immediately become part of the team with a real and substantial role to play.

Academic discipline is less important than the personal qualities an individual brings with them, however a strong interest in and appreciation of finance is important. Whatever the background, it is intellect, personality and zest for life that the firm values the most.

Goldman Sachs evaluate candidates on six core measures – achievement, leadership, commercial focus, analytical thinking , team work and the ability to make an impact. The firm expects commitment, enthusiasm and drive from its employees, but in return, offers unparalleled exposure, early responsibility, significant rewards and unlimited career opportunities.

Goldman Sachs

First job.
Lasting impression.

A chance. An opportunity. A foot in the door. At Goldman Sachs, your first job will give you more. You'll gain access to unparalleled training programmes. Work alongside some of the smartest minds in the financial industry. And gain hands-on experience that will serve you right now, and for years to come. Learn how to make a lasting impression on your career at **gs.com/careers.**

Grant Thornton

Vacancies for around 200 graduates in 2010

- Accountancy
- Finance

Starting salary for 2010
£Competitive
Varies depending on location.

Universities that Grant Thornton plans to visit in 2009-10
Bath, Birmingham, Bristol, Cambridge, Cardiff, Durham, Leeds, London, Loughborough, Manchester, Nottingham, Oxford, Sheffield, Warwick
Please check with your university careers service for details of events.

Application deadline
No official deadline
Early applications are encouraged.

Contact Details
Turn to page 224 now to request more information or visit our new website at www.top100graduateemployers.com

Dave Prentice, 22 - Trainee Auditor
Spotted playing football with workmates at 5.45pm

The truth about graduate careers at Grant Thornton

Everyone's different. So is Grant Thornton. The firm's focus is on being a bold and distinctive leader in its chosen markets and within the accounting profession. Grant Thornton is the UK's fifth largest accountancy firm, with 30 UK offices and 4,000 staff, and provides advice to clients of every description. The firm has a presence in over 100 different countries, so there's also the potential for international exposure.

The firm looks for graduates in audit, tax, business risk services, recovery and reorganisation and actuarial. Trainees are encouraged to take ownership and drive their development by putting their new skills into practice straight away. So whether they are working with a household name or a smaller client, graduates will be face to face with finance directors, government bodies, business owners, influential non-executive directors and well-known financial institutions.

The graduate scheme is designed to help successful applicants become qualified professionals as smoothly and quickly as possible. Graduates start their career with the national induction programme. Further training is held at a dedicated learning centre, where graduates gain essential business, technical and professional skills. Individually focused career development will feature specialist and managerial training, and for some people, progression to partnership.

Trainees work across a variety of sectors and within different teams to develop a range of skills. Secondments and transfers are also commonplace, so there are opportunities to work in different business locations and abroad.

For more information, please go to the website: www.grant-thornton.co.uk/graduates

EXPOSED

The truth about training.

Amy Lucas, 24 - Business Risk Trainee
Snapped preparing her presentation on
the lawn at Bradenham Manor.

"Bad news, I'm afraid. I've been undercover at Grant Thornton for over a month now and I can confirm that all your worst suspicions are true. Take the training. It more than compares with anything other firms can provide. Individual plans, one-to-one support, even a dedicated training centre in a gorgeous 17th century manor house. Study facilities don't get any better than this. It all seems too good to be true, so I'm off to investigate one of their on-campus events. Surely I'll uncover something there…"

Don't take anyone else's word for it. Start your own investigation into a career with the UK's fifth largest accountancy firm. Go to **www.grant-thornton.co.uk/graduates**, talk to us online via our live chat or come along to one of our campus events.

Grant Thornton

Audit • Tax • Advisory

HSBC ◆X►

The world's local bank

www.jobs.hsbc.co.uk/graduates

**Vacancies for around
250 graduates in 2010**

- Finance
- General Management
- Retailing
- Sales

Vacancies also available in Europe,
the USA and Asia.

Starting salary for 2010
£Competitive

**Universities that HSBC
plans to visit in 2009-10**
Aston, Bath, Birmingham,
Cambridge, Cardiff,
Durham, Lancaster,
Leeds, Liverpool, London,
Loughborough, Manchester,
Nottingham, Oxford
Please check with your university
careers service for details of events.

Application deadline
Varies by function
Apply as early as possible.

Contact Details
Turn to page 224 now to request more
information or visit our new website at
www.top100graduateemployers.com

HSBC is one of the largest banking and financial services
organisations in the world, with an international network
comprising over 9,500 offices in 86 countries and territories
in Europe, the Asia-Pacific region, the Americas, the Middle
East and Africa.

HSBC provides a wide range of financial services to over 125 million
customers in the areas of personal financial services; consumer finance;
commercial banking; corporate; investment banking and markets; and
private banking.

The organisation is committed to certain key business principles and values.
They focus on building customer centred relationships, driving long-term profit
and making a positive contribution to the environment. And they believe this is
the reason they've managed to remain a stable, profitable, global business in
these challenging times.

HSBC also believe that challenging times need challenging minds. That's
why only the most exceptional graduates are recruited to join the bank's world
class training programmes. Those graduates can come from any discipline,
but must show the talent and ability to start with HSBC and prepare for
management and executive positions across the business.

These include Commercial Management, European Management, Executive
Management, Operations Management, Retail Management and International
Management.

HSBC also offers a range of internships to promising undergraduates, both in
their first and penultimate year of study.

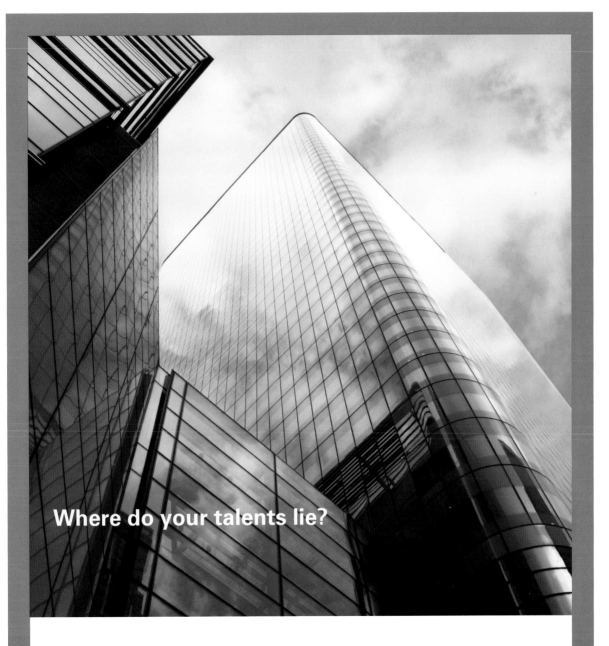

Where do your talents lie?

HSBC are always looking to the future. Our world-class training programmes will help you have a bright future to look forward to. We have a huge range of opportunities, so whatever your academic specialism, you'll find you can really go somewhere with us. Visit our websites to find out more.

• For UK Retail and Commercial visit
www.jobs.hsbc.co.uk/graduates

• For International Management visit
www.hsbc.com/imcareers

HSBC ◆X◆

The world's local bank

Global Businesses

Vacancies for around 200 graduates in 2010

■ Finance

■ Investment Banking

Vacancies also available in the USA and Asia.

The new centre of the world.
Today's China is generating enough economic activity to drive neighbouring emerging markets and to sustain developed economies during the current slowdown. HSBC is acting as the bridge to the rest of the world for this emerging giant.

Starting salary for 2010
£Competitive

Universities that HSBC plans to visit in 2009-10
Bath, Birmingham, Bristol, Cambridge, City, Exeter, London, Loughborough, Nottingham, Oxford, Warwick
Please check with your university careers service for details of events.

Application deadline
13th November 2009

Contact Details
✉ hsbc@graduaterecruitment services.co.uk
Turn to page 224 now to request more information or visit our new website at www.top100graduateemployers.com

The HSBC Group is one of the largest banking and financial services organisations in the world, with 335,000 employees serving customers in 86 countries and territories around the world. With well-established businesses in Europe, Asia-Pacific, the Americas, and the Middle East and Africa, HSBC's unique combination of local knowledge and international expertise reflects its position as 'the world's local bank'.

Through its global businesses – Global Banking and Markets, Global Asset Management, Global Private Banking, and Global Transaction Banking – HSBC offers a comprehensive range of financial services to high net worth individuals, corporate, institutional and government clients worldwide. HSBC takes a long-term approach to their clients and invests time in building strong relationships and understanding each client's financial requirements.

For high calibre, creative and motivated graduates with a genuine interest in global finance, the willingness to take on real responsibility and the desire to join HSBC at this exciting time in its business, HSBC offers a wide range of graduate and internship opportunities in the following business areas: Global Banking and Markets, Global Asset Management, Global Private Banking and Global Transaction Banking.

The extensive and structured programme offers comprehensive business and technical training as well as the opportunity to learn about its international culture and gain a range of transferable soft skills. In addition, graduates will work alongside some of the finest professionals in the industry, taking advantage of the organisation's extensive financial strength and international network.

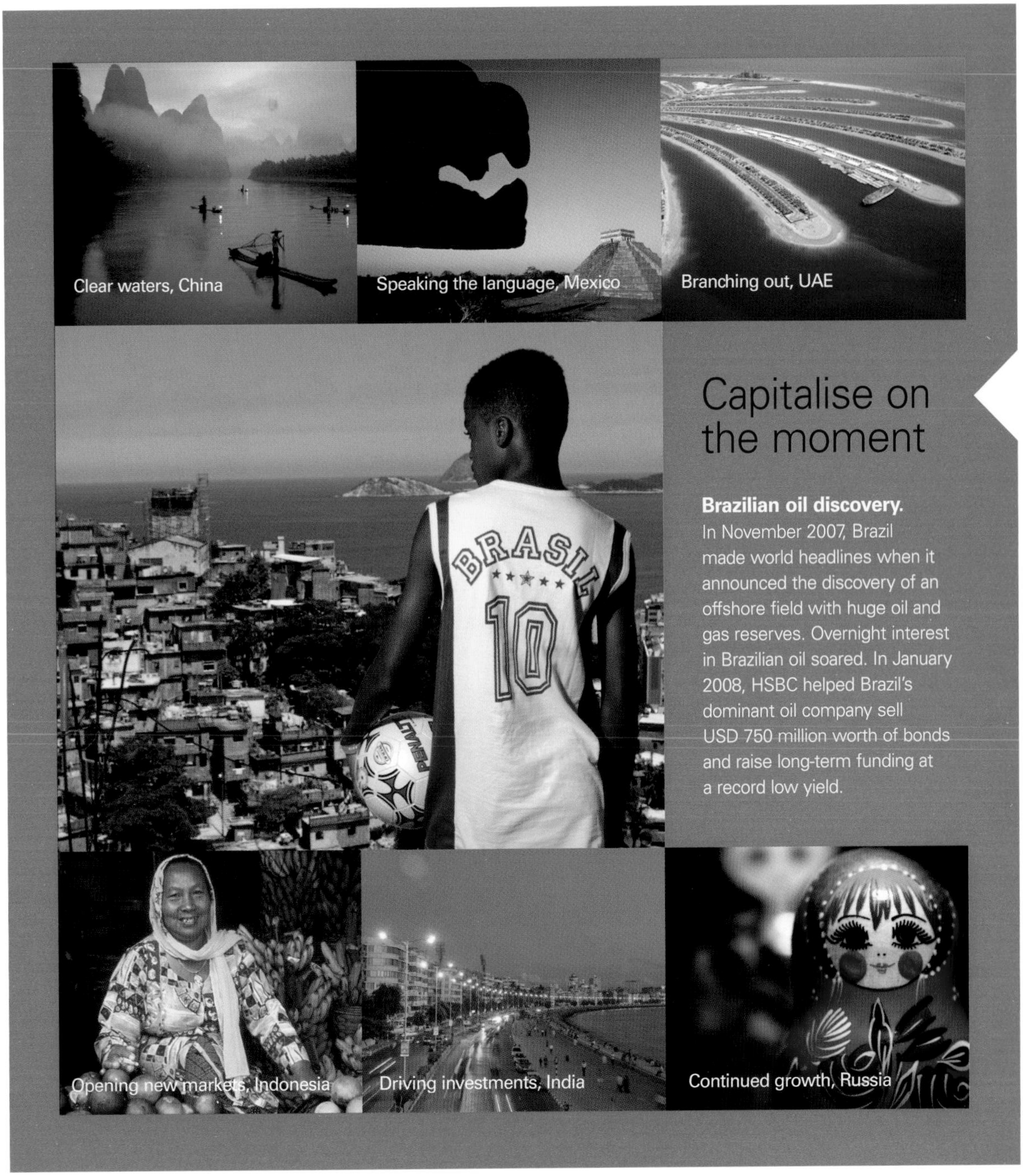
Clear waters, China
Speaking the language, Mexico
Branching out, UAE
Capitalise on the moment
Brazilian oil discovery.
In November 2007, Brazil made world headlines when it announced the discovery of an offshore field with huge oil and gas reserves. Overnight interest in Brazilian oil soared. In January 2008, HSBC helped Brazil's dominant oil company sell USD 750 million worth of bonds and raise long-term funding at a record low yield.
BRASIL
10
PENALTY
Opening new markets, Indonesia
Driving investments, India
Continued growth, Russia

This advert is for recruitment purposes only

Analyst Programmes 2010

More opportunities.
More than an investment bank.

Our position as a pioneer in emerging markets combined with our truly global presence means there has never been a better time for graduates to join HSBC Global Banking and Markets, Global Asset Management, Global Private Banking and Global Transaction Banking. So capitalise on this moment and visit our website to find out more.

www.hsbcnet.com/campusrecruitment

HSBC

The world's local bank

Vacancies for around 200 graduates in 2010

- Accountancy
- Consulting
- Finance
- General Management
- IT
- Sales

Starting salary for 2010
£27,000-£32,000

Universities that IBM plans to visit in 2009-10

Aston, Bath, Birmingham, Bristol, Brunel, Cambridge, Cardiff, Durham, Edinburgh, Exeter, Glasgow, Kent, Lancaster, Leeds, Liverpool, London, Loughborough, Manchester, Newcastle, Northumbria, Nottingham, Nottingham Trent, Oxford, Oxford Brookes, Plymouth, Reading, Sheffield, Southampton, St Andrews, Surrey, Warwick, York
Please check with your university careers service for details of events.

Application deadline
Year-round recruitment

Contact Details

✉ graduate@uk.ibm.com

Turn to page 224 now to request more information or visit our new website at www.top100graduateemployers.com

Smarter Cities — Smarter Banking — Smarter Food

Smarter Energy — Smarter Retail — Smarter Education

Think IBM is just a technology company? Then think again.

In fact, it is an ideas company operating across diverse business streams including Consulting, Sales and Development, IT and Technology, embracing innovation at every turn. Working at IBM, graduates will have the opportunity to change the way the world literally works. Smart cities, smart banking, smart food, smart energy, smart retail, smart education – it is striving to make the planet smarter not only for its clients but for society as a whole.

Join IBM's graduate scheme and successful applicants will find themselves working for a company where they'll be challenged and stretched on a daily basis and where they'll get genuine responsibility from day one. Whether graduates want early contact with clients; apply what they've learnt during their studies to the world of business or they want to work for a company that allows them to give something back to the community – all this and more can be done at IBM.

IBM is looking for people from any degree background who are expecting a 2:1 and who are energetic, adaptable, driven, good team players and have a passion for the area of work they are applying to. Graduates begin their IBM career with a new hire induction programme which is then complemented by personal, business or technical skills training on an ongoing basis. Wherever their career is heading…there are the tools in place at IBM to enable a career to be anything graduates want it to be.

It's no wonder then that they've been voted The Times IT Graduate Employer of Choice for the last 5 years and the Target Graduate Employer of the year for 3 years in a row.

On a smarter planet,
the question isn't what can we do.
The question is what will we do?
Let's build a smarter planet.
ibm.com/start/uk

J.P.Morgan

Vacancies for around 300 graduates in 2010

- Finance
- Investment Banking
- IT

Vacancies also available in Europe, the USA and Asia.

Starting salary for 2010
£Competitive

Universities J.P. Morgan plans to visit in 2009-10
Please check with your university careers service for details of events.

Application deadline
8th November 2009

Contact Details
Turn to page 224 now to request more information or visit our new website at www.top100graduateemployers.com

This is where you need ↗ to be.

From the start, J.P. Morgan's goal has been to become the world's most profitable, respected and influential investment bank. Two hundred years on, this hasn't changed. J.P. Morgan is an industry innovator, forcing the pace of change in global finance, executing "first-class business, in a first-class way".

J.P. Morgan is the investment banking business of JPMorgan Chase, a leading global financial services firm with assets of more than $2.2 trillion and operations in over 60 countries. J.P. Morgan serves the interests of clients who have complex financial needs, whether they are major corporations, governments, private firms, financial institutions, non-profit organisations or private individuals.

The global training programmes combine on-the-job learning with classroom instruction that is on a par with the world's finest business schools. Graduates will gain exposure to different parts of the business, giving a multi-dimensional perspective of the company. As a result, they'll emerge not only with a thorough grounding in a particular business area, but a broad experience of the wider commercial picture and a range of transferable business skills, from project management to team leadership.

J.P. Morgan is looking for team-players and future leaders with exceptional drive, creativity and interpersonal skills. Impeccable academic credentials are important, but so are achievements outside the classroom. Graduate opportunities and internships are available across all areas – Asset Management; Finance; IB Risk; Investment Banking; Operations & Business Services; Sales, Trading & Research; and Technology.

Our
strength
is your
opportunity.

Our strong position in the market has been built on hard work and bright minds. To maintain that strength even in challenging times, we have to keep finding and developing top talent. Which means if you want a platform on which to really advance your career, you should join our award-winning internship and graduate programmes. We can only achieve our goals by making sure you achieve yours. **This is where you need to be.**

Graduate deadline: November 8, 2009
Summer internship deadline: December 13, 2009

Apply via the Europe section of our careers website.

 jpmorgan.com/careers

J.P.Morgan

John Lewis Partnership

www.jlpjobs.com/graduates

Vacancies for around 50 graduates in 2010

- Finance
- General Management
- Retailing
- Sales

Starting salary for 2010
£24,000+

Universities that the John Lewis Partnership plans to visit in 2009-10
Durham, Edinburgh, Exeter, Leeds, Warwick
Please check with your university careers service for details of events.

Application deadline
Year-round recruitment

Contact Details
✉ careers@johnlewis.co.uk

Turn to page 224 now to request more information or visit our new website at www.top100graduateemployers.com

Everyone who works for the John Lewis Partnership (JLP) co–owns the business. That's why, from the moment graduates join, they are Partners, not employees.

One of the UK's leading retail businesses, JLP continued to increase sales in 2009 to £6.97 billion. But it's not only a commercial success story. The company also prides itself on its honesty and integrity.

The Partnership offers two Retail Management schemes (one with John Lewis and one with Waitrose); a Corporate Finance scheme; and two John Lewis Head Office schemes (in Buying and Merchandising). Each one features practical learning, formal courses, short placements and coaching, and gives graduates the training to reach the highest levels of the business.

The John Lewis Retail Management scheme helps graduates reach their first Department Manager position within 12-18 months, then progress into senior store management roles within three to four years. Those who join Waitrose can expect to manage a £multi-million operation as a Department Manager within 12-18 months and run their own store within a few years.

JLP's Finance scheme includes support to study for a CIMA/ACCA qualification and develops the skills to drive the company's growth. Meanwhile, graduates on the Buying scheme can be heading up a team sourcing products globally within three to five years. The John Lewis Head Office scheme in Merchandising is brand new and will begin in Autumn 2010.

Rewards include one of the best profit-sharing schemes around plus discounts, final salary pension scheme and other attractive benefits.

TAKE OWNERSHIP

John Lewis **Waitrose**

Graduate Training Schemes in Retail Management, Buying, Merchandising and Finance

Why be an employee when you could own the business? Here at the John Lewis Partnership, everyone gets the chance to co-own our £6.97 billion organisation. Not only that, they get a say in how it's run and enjoy a share of its profits. Join one of our outstanding training schemes and you could be one of them. Whatever your degree discipline, it's drive, initiative and leadership skills that make you Partnership material.

Vacancies for around 650 graduates in 2010

- Accountancy
- Finance
- Human Resources
- IT

Starting salary for 2010
£Competitive

Universities that KPMG plans to visit in 2009-10
Aberdeen, Aston, Bath, Birmingham, Bristol, Cambridge, Cardiff, City, Dundee, Durham, East Anglia, Essex, Exeter, Edinburgh, Glasgow, Heriot-Watt, Kent, Lancaster, Leeds, Leicester, London, Loughborough, Manchester, Newcastle, Nottingham, Oxford, Plymouth, Reading, Sheffield, Southampton, St Andrews, Strathclyde, Surrey, Sussex, Swansea, Warwick, York
Please check with your university careers service for details of events.

Application deadline
Year-round recruitment

Contact Details
✉ ukfmgraduate@kpmg.co.uk
☎ 0500 664 665

Turn to page 224 now to request more information or visit our new website at www.top100graduateemployers.com

At KPMG, the people make the place. The fact that they have voted them The Sunday Times 'Best Big Company to Work For' two years in a row speaks for itself. A fact that shows KPMG has created a place where everyone feels valued.

What's more, the firm is growing. Since a number of European firms merged to form KPMG Europe LLP, they have become the largest fully-integrated accountancy firm in Europe, offering Audit, Tax and Advisory services to everyone from oil companies to music gurus.

But it's not just what KPMG does that's important. It's the way that they do it. The values don't just live on a wall. They're a way of life, underpinning the way KPMG works with clients and with each other.

So what can graduates look forward to at KPMG? Exposure to clients from day one. Working on challenging projects. And if they're studying for a professional qualification, there's a fantastic support network that includes a mentor and generous study leave.

Despite the focus on qualifications, it's not all work and no play. From flexible working opportunities and CSR days to sabbatical opportunities and free lunches, as The Sunday Times awards show, KPMG is a great place to start a career.

KPMG would like to hear from graduates with at least a 2:1 degree in any discipline. And, once they've applied, they can expect a response on the next working day.

To find out more and to apply, please visit www.kpmg.co.uk/careers

Number one.
Twice.

Straight talking from KPMG.

There's no two ways about it. For the second
year running, our people have voted us The
Sunday Times 'Best Big Company to Work For'.
Stimulating work, fantastic training and
commitment to our local communities are
just some of the reasons why we're different.

We think KPMG is a great place to start your
career – and we're sure you will too.

For more straight talking, visit
www.kpmg.co.uk/careers

AUDIT ▪ TAX ▪ ADVISORY

L'ORÉAL

Vacancies for up to 30 graduates in 2010

- Finance
- Logistics
- Marketing
- Sales

Starting salary for 2010
£27,500

Universities that L'Oréal plans to visit in 2009-10
Bath, Cambridge, Dublin, London, Manchester, Nottingham, Oxford
Please check with your university careers service for details of events.

Application deadline
Year-round recruitment

Contact Details
Turn to page 224 now to request more information or visit our new website at www.top100graduateemployers.com

Graduates joining the L'Oréal management training scheme will be given real responsibility, real challenges and real opportunities from day one. With 130 products sold per second worldwide, L'Oréal offers the most ambitious and entrepreneurial graduates the chance to work with, and become, the most inspirational minds in the business.

L'Oréal's stimulating, motivating and diverse culture is a key factor in making it the No. 1 FMCG employer of choice (Universum Student Survey, 2009). L'Oréal is a committed Investor in People and is ranked among the top 100 most sustainable companies in the world. With brands that reach over 1 billion people in more than 130 countries every year, L'Oréal's global scope is perfectly suited to graduates pursuing dynamic, international business careers.

Each year L'Oréal offers up to 30 high-calibre graduates an individually tailored, 12 month development programme. They are given the opportunity to experience three key areas of L'Oréal's business to help prepare them for future leadership roles. L'Oréal's management trainees could find themselves deep in negotiations with senior buyers at Britain's largest retailers or masterminding an industry-leading launch strategy for one of its world renowned brands. Or perhaps they would be better suited to tackling the logistical challenges presented by a company that produces over 4.5 billion products per year, or to managing part of L'Oréal's €17.5 billion annual sales revenue.

L'Oréal offers roles in commercial, marketing, finance and supply chain. To find out more and to take that first step, please visit www.lorealbusinessclass.co.uk

*BUSINESS STUDENTS, UNIVERSUM SURVEY, 2009

WITHIN SIX MONTHS, WE PUT FREDDIE IN CHARGE OF A £4 MILLION ACCOUNT.

Freddie, Commercial Management Trainee 2008

2:1 Business, University of Bath

RÉAL RESPONSIBILITY

You've got energy, imagination and a passion for business. These same qualities define L'Oréal, the world's largest beauty company. When you join us, you can find this out for yourself. We've developed a training scheme that helps you get under the skin of our company. Because only then will you understand who we really are - a fluid and diverse organisation that recognises individual talents and offers challenges to match.

We offer roles in:
Commercial • Marketing • Supply Chain • Finance

Our internship scheme comprises both summer and sandwich placements in the UK and abroad.
Find out more at **LOREALBUSINESSCLASS.CO.UK**

L'ORÉAL

WELCOME TO THE RÉAL WORLD

INVESTORS IN PEOPLE | Silver

Quality products. Quality people.

Vacancies for around
30 graduates in 2010

- General Management
- Purchasing
- Retailing
- Sales

Vacancies also available in Europe.

Starting salary for 2010
£24,000-£33,000

Universities that Lidl
plans to visit in 2009-10
Aston, Bath, Birmingham,
Bristol, Cardiff, Exeter,
Glasgow, Lancaster,
Liverpool, Loughborough,
Newcastle, Reading,
Sheffield, Southampton,
Strathclyde, Warwick
Please check with your university
careers service for details of events.

Application deadline
Year-round recruitment

Contact Details
Turn to page 224 now to request more
information or visit our new website at
www.top100graduateemployers.com

Lidl is an established international food retailer with more
than 8,000 stores trading across Europe. With over 500
stores in the UK alone they have an impressive schedule
of new store openings.

Lidl are one of the UK's retail success stories. With Lidl's simple retail
philosophy and efficient working practices, they are able to concentrate on what
they do best – providing top quality products at the lowest possible prices.

Lidl's graduate management programme covers all aspects of retail
management from store operations to logistics, supply chain, property and,
most importantly, people management. A structured and hands on approach
to training will allow graduates to take on responsibility from an early stage,
allowing them to make their mark from day one. They will be supported
throughout their training by experienced colleagues.

At Lidl, initiative is encouraged with achievements being recognised; this is
supported by their promise that internal candidates come first in all career
opportunities. In fact, nearly all their senior professionals started their careers
in store operations and have successfully progressed in career paths such
as sales, property, construction, logistics, inclusive of a wide range of head
office positions.

Uncompromising on quality, Lidl look for the same in their graduates.
Lidl is seeking talented and ambitious people who possess good commercial
awareness, are excellent communicators and are highly motivated.

For further information, please visit www.lidl.co.uk

Lidl great place to shop – great place to work.

Anything
but ordinary

www.lidl.co.uk

Linklaters

Vacancies for around 110 graduates in 2010
For training contracts starting in 2012

 Law

Starting salary for 2010
£37,400

Universities Linklaters plans to visit in 2009-10
Birmingham, Bristol, Cambridge, City, Durham, Edinburgh, Exeter, Glasgow, Leeds, Leicester, London, Manchester, Nottingham, Oxford, Sheffield, Southampton, St Andrews, Warwick
Please check with your university careers service for details of events.

Application deadline
See website for full details.

Contact Details
✉ graduate.recruitment@ linklaters.com
Turn to page 224 now to request more information or visit our new website at www.top100graduateemployers.com

Linklaters is a global law firm that advises the world's leading companies, financial institutions and governments on their most important and challenging transactions and assignments. This is an ambitious and innovative firm which aims to become the leading premium global law firm. Its drive to create something new in professional services provides a very special offer to graduates.

While many law firms have strengths in particular areas, Linklaters is strong across the full range of corporate, financial and commercial law. This makes the firm a particularly stimulating place to train as a business lawyer.

The firm recruits graduates from both law and non-law disciplines. Non-law graduates spend a conversion year at law school taking the Graduate Diploma in Law (GDL). All trainees have to complete the Legal Practice Course (LPC) before starting their training contracts. The firm meets the costs of both the GDL and LPC and provides a maintenance grant for both. The training contract is built around four six-month seats or placements in a range of practice areas. The majority of Linklaters' trainees have the opportunity to go on international and/or client secondments.

Linklaters people come from many different backgrounds and cultures; by working together to achieve great things for clients, they are encouraged to achieve their own ambitions and potential. With global opportunities, entrepreneurial freedom and world-class training, Linklaters trainees work alongside some of the world's best lawyers on some of the most challenging deals. The firm has high expectations of its trainees, but the rewards – personal and professional as well as financial – are very high indeed.

Share the thinking.
Linklaters

Do what's
never been
done before.

Linklaters is a global law firm, trusted by the
world's top companies, financial institutions
and governments to solve their most complex
legal issues. When Lehman Brothers went into
administration at 7:56am on 15 September 2008
and the administrators turned to us, our trainee
lawyers were at the very heart of it. We offer a
truly global experience and exposure to work
that has never been done before. To find out
what you could be doing and to read about the
experiences of one of our trainees working on the
Lehman Brothers administration, visit our website
www.linklaters.com/ukgrads

LLOYDS BANKING GROUP

Vacancies for around
150 graduates in 2010

- Finance
- General Management
- Human Resources
- Investment Banking
- IT

Starting salary for 2010
£28,000-£31,000
Salary dependent on programme,
plus sign-on incentive.

Universities that the
Lloyds Banking Group
plans to visit in 2009-10
Bath, Birmingham, Bristol,
Cambridge, Durham,
Edinburgh, Exeter,
Lancaster, Leeds, London,
Loughborough, Manchester,
Nottingham, Oxford,
Sheffield, Warwick, York
Please check with your university
careers service for details of events.

Application deadline
See website for full details.

Contact Details
Turn to page 224 now to request more
information or visit our new website at
www.top100graduateemployers.com

With over 140,000 employees, serving over 30 million customers across 40 countries, Lloyds Banking Group is proud to be one of the UK's leading financial services organisations. With an impressive number of well known brands now in its portfolio, Lloyds Banking Group has an exciting opportunity to shape the future of banking.

With such a diverse portfolio of brands it's no surprise Lloyds Banking Group has the career opportunities to match. With the Graduate Leadership Programme (GLP), Internships, Industrial Placements and Direct Entry Graduate roles, graduates and undergraduates will find a path that both challenges and develops them. Opportunities span across the business, giving a broader understanding of how the organisation works.

The aim of the GLP is to nurture leadership potential, enabling graduates to excel and progress to senior management. Everyone will have access to a dedicated Emerging Talent Manager to support them on their totally unique career journey. Development will include formal training; one to one reviews and placements which are designed to build up management skills and leadership qualities. Depending on programme, study towards professional qualifications will form part of the package.

Successful applicants will need a minimum 2:1, in any discipline, together with all the qualities that make for strong leaders: judgement; drive; the ability to influence and successfully put plans and ideas into action.

As well as exceptional development opportunities, successful applicants can expect a comprehensive rewards and benefits package.

HELP SHAPE THE FUTURE OF BANKING.

Graduate and Undergraduate opportunities

Our vision is to be the best financial services provider in the UK, building a leadership position not on the basis of our size, but on the foundations of reputation and recommendation. We want you to help us achieve this.

Working for Lloyds Banking Group, you will have the opportunity to challenge and develop yourself across some of the UK's leading financial brands and across different business areas.

Whether you come to us on the Graduate Leadership Programme, on an Industrial Placement, as an Intern, or you join us as a Direct Entry Graduate, you will have a role that's specifically designed to challenge you and help you to reach your full potential.

For the opportunity to shape the future of banking, go to www.lloydsbankinggroup.com/graduates

LLOYDS BANKING GROUP

**Vacancies for around
90 graduates in 2010**

For training contracts starting in 2012

▮ Law

Starting salary for 2010
£37,000

**Universities that Lovells
plans to visit in 2009-10**
Birmingham, Bristol,
Cambridge, Durham, Exeter,
Leeds, London, Manchester,
Nottingham, Oxford,
Sheffield, Warwick, York
Please check with your university
careers service for details of events.

Application deadline
31st July 2010

Contact Details
✉ recruit@lovells.com

Turn to page 224 now to request more
information or visit our new website at
www.top100graduateemployers.com

Lovells LLP is one of the largest international legal practices,
with over 3,000 people operating from 27 offices in Europe, Asia
and the United States. The firm is distinguished by its wide
geographic reach and extensive breadth of practice areas,
and it advises many of the world's largest corporations,
financial institutions and government organisations.

Lovells' international strength across a wide range of practice areas gives them
an exceptional reputation not only for corporate transaction work, but for other
specialist areas including dispute resolution, banking, intellectual property,
employment, EU/competition, insurance and tax.

Trainees at Lovells spend six months in four different areas of the practice to
gain as much experience as possible. All trainees must spend six months in
a corporate or finance group, and six months gaining contentious experience
in the firm's dispute resolution practice. There is also the opportunity to go on
secondment to one of the firm's international offices or one of its major clients
in the second year of training. Trainees are offered as much responsibility as
they can handle as well as a comprehensive skills training programme, regular
reviews, appraisals and support. After qualification, continuous training and
professional development remain a priority.

Lovells recruits up to 90 trainee solicitors per year and 50 vacation scheme
students across two summer programmes. Applications are welcome from both
law and non-law candidates. The firm recruits high-calibre graduates who can
demonstrate strong academic and intellectual ability, ambition, drive, strong
communication and interpersonal skills, and a professional/commercial attitude.

Lovells

VENTURE
MYRIAD
ASTUTE
BELONG

www.lovells.com/graduates

Myriad n. an indefinitely great number
– A myriad of clients and practice areas.

We tailor our training contracts to fit our trainee solicitors perfectly. We continually invest in our people to successfully serve our large client base across a diverse range of business sectors. As a graduate of the highest calibre you will receive a training contract that will empower you. Following your training you will have the confidence, skills and knowledge to handle the most complex and diverse legal work.

Our firmwide team delivers quality as standard and is committed to our clients' ongoing success. To find out more about Venture, Myriad, Astute and Belong at Lovells visit our graduate website www.lovells.com/graduates

YOUR M&S

www.marksandspencer.com/gradcareers

Vacancies for around 100 graduates in 2010

- IT
- Purchasing
- Retailing

Starting salary for 2010
£24,000+

Universities that Marks & Spencer plans to visit in 2009-10
Please check with your university careers service for details of events.

Application deadline
December 2009

Contact Details
Turn to page 224 now to request more information or visit our new website at www.top100graduateemployers.com

When it comes to offering graduates a thorough grounding in retail, the Marks & Spencer scheme is hard to beat.

The scheme involves taking on three or four placements over the course of around 12 months. Alongside this on-the-job training, graduates receive classroom tuition, designed to help them develop expert knowledge, as well as personal skills in areas such as negotiation and leadership. And they will be making real decisions about real business issues from day one.

By the end of the scheme, they should have everything they need to take on their first big management role. That could mean leading a team of people or running an area of the business worth millions of pounds. In all likelihood, it will mean both.

Most M&S graduates join them in a store-based role, and are placed on a fast-track route into senior level retail management. If everything goes as planned, then this will mean running a small store – or a whole department of a large one – after about a year.

There are also places available in a range of head office areas, including IT, design, buying, merchandising, garment and food technology, and product development, as well as opportunities for undergraduates to do 12-month business placements.

M&S aren't just looking for any graduates. They're looking for the best around. People with the drive and ambition to make the most of all the opportunities on offer. And people who can match the energy, vision and ideas that have kept M&S at the forefront of their industry for so long.

This is not just any graduate scheme.

www.marksandspencer.com/gradcareers

MARS
incorporated

Vacancies for around
30+ graduates in 2010

- Engineering
- Finance
- General Management
- Purchasing
- Research & Development
- Sales

Discover a world
where the only string attached
to freedom is responsibility.

Starting salary for 2010
£29,000+

Universities that Mars
plans to visit in 2009-10
Bath, Bristol,
Cambridge, Edinburgh,
Leeds, Loughborough,
Manchester, Nottingham,
Oxford, Warwick
Please check with your university
careers service for details of events.

Application deadline
14th February 2010
See website for full details.

Contact Details
Turn to page 224 now to request more
information or visit our new website at
www.top100graduateemployers.com

Mars®, Uncle Ben's®, Snickers®, Whiskas®, M&M's®, Dolmio®, Twix®, Pedigree®, Maltesers®, Extra®, Airwaves®... these are just some of the household name brands that form the global, $40bn Mars portfolio, making it one of the world's biggest consumer goods companies.

But it's the unique culture that separates Mars from the rest. Based on their five principles, over 60,000 associates in more than 106 countries enjoy the degree of freedom and responsibility unparalleled in the business world.

Still a family-run business and entirely privately owned, Mars is able to invest their own profits in developing the organisation. This means associates have the freedom to think differently and do things normal convention wouldn't allow. With this being the case, Mars graduates get all the support, freedom and responsibility they need. But ultimately, it's the graduates themselves that drive their projects forward, and shape things as they go along.

Whether their talents lie in research and development, engineering, sales, marketing, finance, procurement or general management, Mars' renowned development programmes offer responsibility right from the very first day. Graduates get to work on real projects, carefully chosen to suit their development needs. Support in the pursuit of professional qualifications with financial sponsorship, study leave and regular two-way feedback is a given.

Structured around a rigorous training curriculum and strong individual mentoring relationships, the programmes offer talented individuals an opportunity to take their career in their own hands while benefiting from the years of experience in developing some of the UK's leading managers.

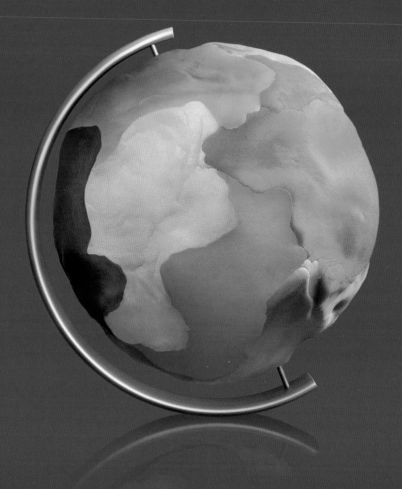

Discover a world which
people are constantly shaping.

We're still the same family-owned business that started out back in 1911, only now we're quite a bit bigger. With an annual turnover of $40 billion, 60,000 employees, and a presence in 106 countries, we're able to offer our graduates the strength, stability and freedom to grow with fewer restrictions. Mars' renowned development programmes offer real responsibility right from the very first day. Together, we'll shape our own destiny.

MARS® SNICKERS® M&M'S® TWIX® WHISKAS® PEDIGREE® SHEBA® CESAR® UNCLE BEN'S® DOLMIO® EXTRA® AIRWAVES®

Freedom takes courage. We take the courageous.      mars.co.uk

i'm lovin' it

www.mcdonalds.co.uk/careers

Vacancies for around 150 graduates in 2010

■ General Management
■ Retailing

Starting salary for 2010
£18,500-£21,500

Universities McDonald's plans to visit in 2009-10
Please check with your university careers service for details of events.

Application deadline
Year-round recruitment

Contact Details
✉ mcdcareers@uk.mcd.com
☎ 020 8700 7007

Turn to page 224 now to request more information or visit our new website at www.top100graduateemployers.com

Forget the myth that says McDonald's only offers McJobs. The reality is very different – and far more interesting. McDonald's management careers offer exceptional challenge and support, some excellent rewards and all the potential of a world-famous brand.

Their 20-week management development programme prepares graduates for running a restaurant – Business Management as they call it. This is commercial management in its fullest sense. Graduates gain valuable operational experience in the restaurants, and, as importantly, benefit from wide-ranging commercial exposure. They cover everything from leadership and people development to cash control and profit maximisation.

Provided they excel on the programme, within a few years of joining, graduates could be managing a £million business with a 60-strong team: a McDonald's restaurant. After that they join a management career path that could lead to Executive team level. Naturally, not everyone will climb that high. But as long as they have leadership potential and can make the most of the award-winning training, there's no reason why graduates shouldn't set their sights high.

McDonald's urges graduates to do some soul-searching before applying. McDonald's managers set the tone of their restaurants, bringing the best out of their team. To build their businesses, they have to display energy, commitment and hard work every day. And they need to combine both decisiveness and sensitivity; ideas and action. Only by blending all these qualities will graduates excel on one of the most stimulating management development programmes around.

I love that I can go right to the top.

PAUL, ESSEX

MY MᶜJOB

Trainee Business Managers

With management training that reflects the latest thinking and wins awards, your career can go as far as you want it to.

Apply at mcdonalds.co.uk/careers

McKinsey&Company

www.mckinsey.com/careers

Vacancies for no fixed quota **of graduates in 2010**

■ **Consulting**

Vacancies also available elsewhere in the world.

Starting salary for 2010
£Competitive

Universities that McKinsey & Company plans to visit in 2009-10

Bath, Bristol, Cambridge, Dublin, Edinburgh, London, Oxford, St Andrews
Please check with your university careers service for details of events.

Application deadline
1st November 2009

Contact Details
✉ london_opportunities@ mckinsey.com
☎ 020 7961 7070

Turn to page 224 now to request more information or visit our new website at www.top100graduateemployers.com

McKinsey & Company helps world-leading clients in the public, private and third sectors to meet their biggest strategic, operational and organisational challenges. Their goal is to provide distinctive and long-lasting performance improvements – in short, it is about having an impact. Making a difference.

As a consultant in this truly global firm, graduates will have the opportunity to work with colleagues and clients from all around the world. They will come into contact with CEOs, government leaders and the foremost charitable organisations, and work together with them on their most exciting and challenging issues.

Working as part of a small team, and dedicated to one project at a time, graduates will be fully involved from the very start of their first project. No two weeks will be the same: from gathering and analysing data, to interviewing stakeholders or presenting findings to clients, the range of industries and business issues to which successful applicants have exposure will mean that they are constantly acquiring new skills and experience. Bright, motivated newcomers can expect their ideas and opinions to be encouraged and valued, right from day one.

Graduates will also enjoy world-class personal and professional development. Formal training programmes, coupled with a culture of mentoring and coaching, will provide the best possible support to reach their full potential.

Working in consulting is challenging, but McKinsey encourages a healthy work-life balance. Successful applicants will find like-minded individuals, and a thriving range of groups, initiatives and events that bring people together.

Metaswitch
Networks

www.metaswitch.com/careers

Vacancies for around 30 graduates in 2010

 IT

Vacancies also available in the USA.

Starting salary for 2010
£30,000

Universities that Metaswitch Networks plans to visit in 2009-10
Bath, Cambridge, Durham, Edinburgh, London, Oxford, St Andrews, Warwick, York
Please check with your university careers service for details of events.

Application deadline
Year-round recruitment

Contact Details
✉ recruit@metaswitch.com
☎ 020 8366 1177

Turn to page 224 now to request more information or visit our new website at www.top100graduateemployers.com

Metaswitch Networks were previously known as Data Connection. They have a new name to go with their next phase of exciting growth and increased opportunities. Metaswitch Networks is one of the world's leading communications technology companies, working with companies such as Cisco, Microsoft, Ericsson, AT&T and British Telecom. For the past six years, they have consistently been in the top ten of the Sunday Times '100 Best Companies to Work For'.

Graduates can be assured of a wide range of challenging opportunities. From day one, they will be working as part of a high calibre, closely knit team, working on the design and development of complex software or hardware. The speed with which successful applicants progress will be determined by their own ability and desire, not by a constraining, formal career structure. They can continue to develop their career further in a technical role, or move into project and people management, sales, marketing or product management.

At Metaswitch Networks, on-the-job training, backed up by constant constructive feedback, will form the basis of graduate development. Add to this an array of internal and external courses, and new starters will gain all of the skills they need to succeed.

Metaswitch Networks recruit exceptionally bright and energetic graduates and postgraduates from any degree discipline. Graduates do not need prior computing experience. However, an enquiring mind and the proven ability to solve complex problems are essential. The right candidate will have an outstanding academic record: all A grades at A level (or equivalent) and a good degree.

Do you enjoy solving complex problems?

If so, a career at Metaswitch Networks could be for you.

ou may have known us as Data Connection. We now have a ew name to go with our next phase of exciting growth and ncreased opportunities. Metaswitch Networks is one of the orld's leading communications technology companies, providing arrier systems and software solutions to a customer base that ncludes Cisco, Microsoft, Ericsson, AT&T and British Telecom.

Ve have a new brand and lots of new ideas, but our core values re the same. We recruit exceptionally bright graduates and ostgraduates from any degree discipline, and then train them o become world-class professionals and managers, across our ngineering, support, product management, sales and marketing rganisations.

or the past six years, we have consistently been in the top ten f the Sunday Times '100 Best Companies to Work For'. Our lanned growth will bring a larger investment in technology and eople development, more exciting and innovative projects and he opportunity for international travel. There's never been a etter time to join Metaswitch Networks.

in us for the next phase of our exciting growth. Take control f your future by visiting www.metaswitch.com/careers

ur Career. Your Choices. Your Company.

Any Degree Discipline

£30k plus Benefits

Tailored Training and Development

No Closing Date

Your Career. You will have the freedom and flexibility to drive your career at the pace and direction that you choose.

Your Choices. Where you go in Metaswitch Networks is determined by you and your ability. You will work hard, with bright people, in a supportive and stimulating environment where you can choose from a variety of challenging opportunities.

Your Company. A substantial part of the company is owned by an Employee Benefit Trust (EBT) which distributes a share of profit to all employees, rewarding you for your contribution. In addition, we also operate an employee share option plan, which further provides ownership incentives to our people.

METROPOLITAN POLICE

Working together for a safer London

www.metpolicecareers.co.uk

Vacancies for around TBC graduates in 2010

- Accountancy
- Finance
- General Management
- Human Resources
- IT
- Marketing
- Media
- Research & Developement

Starting salary for 2010
£Competitive
See website for full details.

Universities that the Met plans to visit in 2009-10
London
Please check with your university careers service for details of events.

Application deadline
Year-round recruitment

Contact Details
Turn to page 224 now to request more information or visit our new website at www.top100graduateemployers.com

The Metropolitan Police Service is continually evolving and improving to respond to the needs of millions of people of all nationalities, faiths and cultures who visit, live and work in London. The organisation aims to deliver quality policing that reduces crime – and the fear of crime – across the capital. It is also recognised on a global scale as a leading authority on policing today.

The Met today is a far cry from the organisation that was founded in 1829 by Home Secretary Sir Robert Peel. Back then, there were just 1,000 officers looking after a population of 2 million. Now, there are some 54,000 officers and staff working as one team to make the streets safer for 7.2 million Londoners in 32 boroughs across 620 square miles.

As one of the capital's largest employers, the Met is committed to having a workforce that reflects the community it serves. People join from all kinds of backgrounds, bringing all sorts of skills and experience to a huge diversity of roles. As well as frontline officers, the Met employs 14,000 police staff who carry out vital work such as answering emergency calls, forensics, handling finances or harnessing the latest advancements in technology.

But London can only be policed with the trust and respect of all Londoners, so it's essential that everyone who joins has the sensitivity to work effectively with the many different communities that make up the capital.

Making London safer is uniquely challenging but uniquely rewarding. Good salaries are supplemented by attractive benefits including a superb pension and opportunities for career progression.

L

AST

WEEK AN

OPTICIAN

ASKED ME TO

BE AN EYE WITNESS

Volunteer Police Officers

16 hours a month – London

Whether your job involves testing eyes, brakes or software, there's no more rewarding way to spend your free time than as a Special Constable with the Met.

It's a distinctive volunteer role that will help you develop a wide range of transferable skills such as problem solving, negotiating and decision making. So you'll grow both personally and professionally.

We'll give you in-depth training as well as the same powers and uniform as regular Police Officers. Volunteering just 16 hours a month, you'll gain many valuable experiences you simply can't get anywhere else.

Download an application form today at **www.metpolicecareers.co.uk/specials**

Alternatively, text SPECIAL157 to 84880 for an application form or call 0845 727 2212 Mon-Fri, 9am-4pm, quoting 250/09 for more information.

WHATEVER YOU DO, DO THIS.

 **METROPOLITAN POLICE** Working together for a safer London

SECURITYSERVICE MI5

www.mi5careers.gov.uk

Vacancies for around TBC graduates in 2010

- Engineering
- Finance
- Human Resources
- IT

Starting salary for 2010
£Varies by function
See website for full details.

Universities that MI5 plans to visit in 2009-10
Please check with your university careers service for details of events.

Application deadline
Year-round recruitment

Contact Details
Turn to page 224 now to request more information or visit our new website at www.top100graduateemployers.com

MI5 is the UK's security intelligence agency. Through the collection, dissemination and analysis of intelligence, they protect the UK from threats such as terrorism and espionage. To do this takes talented people from a range of backgrounds.

MI5 offers a range of careers. So, whatever degree graduates might have, it's likely there's a role that suits their skills and abilities. MI5 also look for a strong range of personal qualities.

Many graduates join as intelligence officers. This demanding and rewarding role involves assessing or investigating threats to national security. Most intelligence officers move departments every two to three years so as well as investigative work a career could include policy, personnel, finance or operational work. Intelligence officers have their own areas of responsibility but work as part of a team.

There are also career opportunities as intelligence analysts, administrative assistants, business support officers, electronic technicians, working in our language unit, mobile surveillance officers and IT roles.

As well as vital and varied work, there are lots of other benefits. Training and development programmes give a broader understanding of the organisation and will equip staff with the specialist skills needed to make the most of the career opportunities available. The salary and rewards are competitive and include a generous pension scheme and holiday entitlement. Graduates joining the organisation can also look forward to working with people from a range of backgrounds in a friendly, team orientated working environment with a strong sense of camaraderie.

Careful examination pays off.

The way that clouds constantly change their shape in the sky has made them an object of fascination throughout human history. But this infinite variability was also one of the reasons they were able to defy scientific investigation for so long. In fact, it was not until the beginning of the 19th century that clouds were formally categorised. How quickly can you get to the information that matters? Published in 1803, Luke Howard's *Essay on the Modification of Clouds* outlines the three principal categories of cloud – cirrus, cumulus and stratus – that are still used by meteorologists today. Find out more about becoming one of our Intelligence Officers. Howard's masterstroke was to see how the principles of natural history classification could be applied to this most ephemeral of phenomena. Visit www.mi5careers.gov.uk/intelligence By providing his categories with Latin names (Latin then being the language of scholarship), he was also able to create a system that transcended national borders and thus provided a solid foundation for scientific study.

Your potential. Our passion.™

Microsoft®

www.microsoft.com/uk/graduates

Vacancies for around 20 graduates in 2010

- IT
- Marketing
- Sales

Starting salary for 2010
£26,000
Plus a sign-on bonus.

Universities Microsoft plans to visit in 2009-10
Aston, Bath, Brunel, Kent, Lancaster, Leeds, Loughborough, Manchester, Nottingham, Reading, Southampton, Surrey, Warwick
Please check with your university careers service for details of events.

Application deadline
January 2010

Contact Details
✉ gradrec@microsoft.com
Turn to page 224 now to request more information or visit our new website at www.top100graduateemployers.com

Microsoft have created an environment where people can do their best. Hard work is expected, but graduates and students are free to satisfy their intellectual curiosity. Microsoft is somewhere people can think along new lines, explore truly exciting technologies and actually enjoy spending time.

The people who flourish at Microsoft are natural communicators with inquisitive natures, a passion for technology and an instinctive understanding of customers. But what really sets them apart is a drive that raises them above the average whether they join commercial or technical business groups.

The 'Microsoft Academy for University Hires' (MACH) provides the perfect transition between academic and professional life. Although challenging, it equips graduates with the professional skills and know-how required for a rewarding and successful career at Microsoft. Graduates will genuinely tackle unchartered territory, whether working in a technical, sales or marketing role. It might mean discovering how others work or thinking along new lines. Either way, successful applicants will be stepping outside their comfort zone.

The graduate programme includes residential courses at international locations and self-directed learning. Graduates will be given real responsibility, whilst also having the support of managers and mentors throughout. The basic requirements are a 2:1, creativity, vision, people skills, an inquiring mind and a willingness to learn.

The emphasis during student placements in Reading or London is on supplementing theory learnt at university with real, practical experience. The 48 week scheme starts in July with a week-long induction. Training can include residential courses and self-directed learning.

How do you see the future?

Do you see it doing what you love, at a company where you're valued? Having your talent nurtured and your ideas encouraged? Learning, improving and developing in a dozen different ways? If so, you see it at Microsoft.

The Microsoft Academy for University Hires (MACH) sets talented, driven people on the path to success. The two-year programme is designed to give graduates the best possible start in a range of careers within our technical, sales and marketing groups. It provides the theoretical and practical skills you need to complement your academic achievements. The business acumen to make a difference at the highest levels. And ultimately, the ability to deliver solutions that touch people's lives worldwide.

See what else lies ahead at Microsoft.
www.microsoft.com/uk/graduates

Your potential. Our passion.™

Microsoft®

MINISTRY OF DEFENCE

DEFENCE ENGINEERING AND SCIENCE GROUP

Vacancies for around 120 graduates in 2010

■ Engineering

■ IT

Starting salary for 2010
£Competitive

Universities that the MOD plans to visit in 2009-10
Please check with your university careers service for details of events.

Application deadline
See website for full details.

Contact Details

✉ sit-desgmktman@mod.uk

☎ 01225 449368

Turn to page 224 now to request more information or visit our new website at www.top100graduateemployers.com

The Defence Engineering and Science Group (DESG) is the team of thousands of engineers and scientists working within the Ministry of Defence.

The UK needs modern battle winning forces to defend its interests and to contribute to strengthening international peace and security. Cutting edge engineering and science is a critical component in supporting this effort. The MOD is proud to offer graduates the opportunity to join what is probably the very best graduate development scheme for engineers and scientists in the UK: The Ministry of Defence, Defence Engineering and Science Graduate Scheme.

This prestigious graduate scheme is accredited by: IET, IMechE, RINA, IoP, RAeS and ICE and has been an industry leader for almost thirty years, launching hundreds of graduates into satisfying careers in engineering and science. It is because of the requirement to safeguard the UK and its interests that the DESG can offer a huge range and depth of development opportunities – making it a market leader.

Moreover, it is the quality of the training programme, the accelerated path to chartership, personal mentoring and huge investment in each graduate that sets this apart from competitors in the engineering and science field. The DESG Graduate Scheme is a carefully structured but flexible training programme; enabling each graduate to get the most from a series of training courses and work placements (including placements with industry).

Through this unique scheme each graduate is able to further their professional development – making it possible for them to gain tremendous engineering or science experience and to achieve Chartered status within just four years.

MINISTRY OF DEFENCE

DESG
DEFENCE ENGINEERING
AND SCIENCE GROUP

UFO

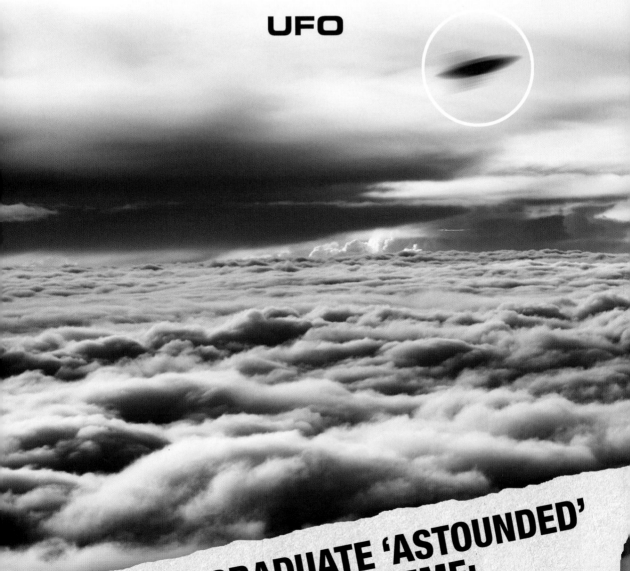

-NGINEERING GRADUATE 'ASTOUNDED' BY SIGHTING OF MOD SCHEME:

MoD Releases Further Files

An Engineering Graduate, accompanied by a science colleague, has spotted what is probably the very best graduate development scheme for engineers and scientists available in the UK - fully accredited by IMechE, IET, ICE, RINA, IoP, RAeS and IMarEST.

The Ministry of Defence has admitted total involvement and has confirmed the sighting as genuine. In an official statement the MoD's Defence Engineering and Science Group said:

'These are UFOs (Unique, First-class Opportunities) in connection with technologies of breathtaking speed, power and capacity; providing a decisive technological edge.

We offer you many benefits including:

1. Massive investment in you. Over and above your salary, the investment in support of your personal professional development will be around 20k per year!

2. An accelerated path to Chartered status in your engineering or science profession; with the DESG it's possible for you to achieve professional Chartership in just four years.

3. A truly rewarding career; MoD projects are fascinating, valuable, unique and sometimes highly classified.

Degree Disciplines required: A multitude of engineering disciplines - also sciences with an emphasis on Physics.

Applications: Apply on-line via our website (Click 'How to Apply') See www.desg.mod.uk for closing date.

Undergraduate Sponsorship: Visit our website (Click 'Student Opportunities' for details).'

www.desg.mod.uk

Morgan Stanley
WORLD WISE

www.morganstanley.com/careers

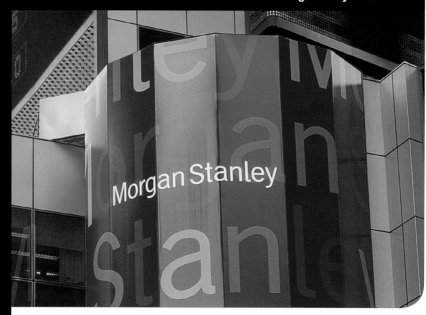

Vacancies for around 200 graduates in 2010

- Finance
- Investment Banking
- IT

Vacancies also available in Europe, the USA and Asia.

Starting salary for 2010
£Competitive

Universities that Morgan Stanley plans to visit in 2009-10
Please check with your university careers service for details of events.

Application deadline
9th November 2009

Contact Details
✉ graduaterecruitmenteurope@morganstanley.com

Turn to page 224 now to request more information or visit our new website at www.top100graduateemployers.com

Morgan Stanley is a leading global financial services firm providing a wide range of investment banking, securities, investment management and wealth management services.

The firm has over 40,000 employees in more than 600 offices in 36 countries, serving clients worldwide including corporations, governments, institutions and individuals. Their services include: investment banking advice on mergers and acquisitions, privatisations and financial restructuring; debt and equity underwriting; sales and trading in all the world's major markets; and market leading research.

Analyst training at Morgan Stanley quickly makes effective professionals. The training covers not only how to use Morgan Stanley's unsurpassed data resources and analytic tools but also enables recruits to gain a thorough understanding of the firm's culture, its core values and key products.

Graduates work on a team under the direct guidance of senior professionals who are among the best in their fields. They will give as much responsibility as graduates can handle, in an environment that affords exciting opportunities to work with a wide variety of clients in different industries, helping them to make strategic decisions involving capital raising, research or trading issues at the highest level. Training is not limited to the first weeks or months on the job but is ongoing throughout their career at Morgan Stanley.

Morgan Stanley accepts applications from all degree disciplines. However some business areas will require graduates to have a degree of a quantitative or analytical nature and they should in general have a keen interest in financial services and markets. A high achiever who thrives on integrity, intellectual curiosity and the desire to work in a congenial atmosphere with like-minded people.

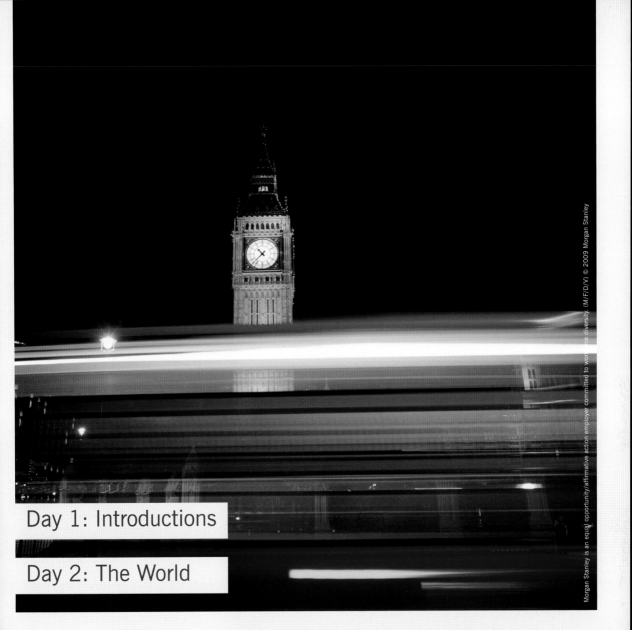

Day 1: Introductions

Day 2: The World

The faster your career grows, the smaller the globe will seem.
At Morgan Stanley, solving complex challenges and fueling economic growth across continents is what we do. On any given day, you might be facilitating and underwriting transactions, or providing liquidity and capital for a growing global economy. We offer you a structured path to success, which means you'll quickly gain unprecedented exposure to every aspect of the financial world. Moreover, we'll give you the opportunity to become involved in making a real difference. And we'll provide you with the training, mobility, and responsibility to do it. If you have the perspective to face today's global challenges, we'd like to talk to you.

To find out more about career opportunities at Morgan Stanley and to hear from recent hires visit: **www.morganstanley.com/careers**

Morgan Stanley
WORLD WISE

**Vacancies for around
135 graduates in 2010**

- Accountancy
- Engineering
- Finance
- General Management
- IT
- Logistics
- Purchasing
- Other

Starting salary for 2010
£24,000+
Plus package.

**Universities Network Rail
plans to visit in 2009-10**
Bath, Birmingham, Bristol,
Cambridge, Cardiff,
Durham, Edinburgh,
Leeds, Liverpool, London,
Loughborough, Manchester,
Newcastle, Nottingham,
Oxford, Reading, Sheffield,
Southampton, Strathclyde,
Surrey, Warwick, York
Please check with your university
careers service for details of events.

Application deadline
January 2010

Contact Details
✉ enquiry@
networkrailgraduates.co.uk
☎ 0845 601 4228
Turn to page 224 now to request more
information or visit our new website at
www.top100graduateemployers.com

No other organisation has such a marked and visible impact
on the lives of people across Britain. Responsible for tracks,
signals, tunnels, bridges, viaducts, level crossings and stations,
Network Rail touch millions of lives across the nation, every day,
and over the next ten years they are expected to grow by 30%.

With such an unprecedented period of change ahead, Network Rail is investing
£34.6bn over the next five years to deliver the growth the nation needs.
Schemes like the £2.3bn investment in Crossrail, the £600m development
of Birmingham New Street station, the £5.5bn upgrade and expansion
of Thameslink, and the recently completed £9bn West Coast Main Line
improvement project. These are some of the largest engineering projects going
on across Europe today. They will redefine the travel network.

Few other graduate programmes can boast such huge responsibility. After a
period of induction, graduates will gain valuable experience on a range of
placements, and they'll have real control over the pace and content of their
progression. Obviously there are many great opportunities for engineers, but
the Network Rail Graduate Programme has a vast range of schemes that include
contracts & procurement, operations and customer service, project management
and information management (IT).

Network Rail takes training and development very seriously; after all, graduates
are about to become the future leaders of the organisation. Whichever the
specialism, successful applicants will work towards professional qualifications and
will receive regular reviews of their performance and development. Wherever they
join, graduates will be able to see the impact of their work around them, every
day. As they become part of the organisation that helps to define the nation.

www.ngdp.co.uk

The ngdp is a two–year graduate management development programme, run by the Improvement and Development Agency (The IDeA) that is designed to develop future managers and leaders in local government.

It was set up to provide local government with the high calibre managers their communities need, and to give committed graduates the training, qualifications and opportunities to make a real difference. Local government is the largest employer in the UK, with over two million staff in over 400 local authorities and in excess of 500 different occupational areas.

Over 450 graduates have completed the programme and many now hold important managerial and policy roles in the sector. Local government is going through many positive changes at present and as a national management trainee on the ngdp, graduates will be a key component of these changes.

The national programme framework is built on a series of placements in key areas of a participating council and offers a range of experiences and challenges which will provide a broad understanding of many aspects of local government in strategy, front line service and support. Although employed by a participating authority, on a 2-year fixed term contract, graduates will benefit from being part of a national programme group; participate in a national induction event and study for a postgraduate qualification. Mentoring is also provided on a regional basis and support is provided through local authorities, national networks and a dedicated central ngdp team.

The programme has taken graduates in many different directions, and will enable them to be part of an exciting period of opportunity which not only recommends change, but actually makes it happen.

NATIONAL GRADUATE DEVELOPMENT PROGRAMME
ngdp.
FOR LOCAL GOVERNMENT

BOROUGH OF FINSBURY

REAL CHANGE

The **ngdp** is a graduate development programme run by the Improvement and Development Agency (IDeA). It's designed to provide local government with the high-calibre managers their communities need, and give committed graduates the training, qualifications and opportunities to make a real difference. Over two years you'll undertake a series of placements, covering front line services, support services and strategy. You'll receive a competitive salary and benefits. You'll also get to study for a fully funded post-graduate qualification. But most of all, you'll get the chance to see your ideas have real impact. To find out more, visit www.ngdp.co.uk or call 0845 222 0250 for a brochure.

Real life. Real work.

www.ngdp.co.uk

Vacancies for around 240 graduates in 2010

- ▮ Finance
- ▮ General Management
- ▮ Human Resources
- ▮ IT

Starting salary for 2010
£22,222

Universities that the NHS plans to visit in 2009-10

Aston, Bath, Birmingham, Bradford, Brunel, Cambridge, Durham, East Anglia, Hull, Lancaster, Leeds, Leicester, Liverpool, London, Loughborough, Manchester, Newcastle, Northumbria, Nottingham, Nottingham Trent, Oxford, Plymouth, Reading, Sheffield, Southampton, York
Please check with your university careers service for details of events.

Application deadline
Early December 2009

Contact Details
Turn to page 224 now to request more information or visit our new website at www.top100graduateemployers.com

Lead the way.

It's what we do.
It's what we want you to do.

As career opportunities go there aren't many that can offer you the chance to tackle some of the greatest challenges of our time. Like how can Europe's largest employer reduce its impact on UK carbon emissions? How will the credit crunch affect the provision of healthcare services in the UK? How will the NHS transform itself and improve patient care through quality and innovation?

These are exactly the sort of questions managers in the NHS are looking to answer. And this world-class Graduate Management Training Scheme promises to give emerging leaders the answers with comprehensive training and development, essential in preparation for one of the toughest yet rewarding careers out there.

Employing 1.3 million people and responsible for an annual budget of £100 billion – career opportunities really don't get much bigger than this. It takes nothing less than total dedication to handle the complexity and sheer scope of an organisation that looks after 60 million people from their very first breath.

Individuals can choose to join the NHS scheme in either: Finance, HR, General Management or Informatics Management, developing essential skills that could make a difference to the lives of millions of people. After gaining postgraduate and professional qualifications together with real work experience through NHS placements across England, they'll wield real influence within one of the most innovative and forward thinking organisations in the world.

The NHS welcomes applicants from all backgrounds who have or are expecting at least a 2:2 degree or equivalent (please refer to www.nhsgraduates.co.uk for eligibility criteria). Postgraduates, mature students and those working within the NHS are also encouraged to apply.

There's a reason why we only accepted 5% of applications last year.

By only taking on dedicated individuals who are truly up for the challenge, we ensure we get the best people to manage the nation's healthcare system. Taking on a leadership role in a workforce this big isn't easy, but if you're ambitious, talented and committed, the possibilities for career progression are limitless. Providing a country's healthcare requires nothing less than the best, so if you know that you'll only ever thrive in a career that challenges and excites, and you are sure you have what it takes to succeed, then join our scheme and make your mark.

Make a real difference to the people around you.

NHS Graduate Management Training Scheme   www.nhsgraduates.co.uk

Lead the way

npower

Vacancies for around 30 graduates in 2010

- Engineering
- Finance
- General Management
- IT

Starting salary for 2010
£25,000

Universities that npower plans to visit in 2009-10

Bath, Birmingham, Bristol, Cambridge, Cardiff, Durham, Lancaster, Leeds, Liverpool, London, Loughborough, Manchester, Newcastle, Nottingham, Oxford, Sheffield, Southampton, Swansea, Warwick

Please check with your university careers service for details of events.

Application deadline
See website for full details.

Contact Details
✉ graduate.team@RWEnpower.com

Turn to page 224 now to request more information or visit our new website at www.top100graduateemployers.com

npower is one of the UK's leading integrated energy companies, and part of RWE, one of Europe's largest utility groups. As Britain's brightest energy company, npower gives creative and ambitious graduates the chance to work on exciting projects.

They operate one of the largest portfolios of power generating plants in the UK and supply electricity and gas to more than 6.8 million residential and business customers. And they are also one of the leaders in the search for renewable power sources, having developed the UK's first major offshore wind farm, and operating hydroelectric power stations in Scotland and Wales, using advanced communications and forecasting technology. They are committed to conducting their business with a sense of responsibility for the environment, their customers and for the communities in which they work.

As Britain's brightest energy company they are looking for Britain's brightest graduates. They have opportunities in engineering, general business management, finance, business analysis, risk and IS within RWE IT UK. npower will give those who bring enthusiasm, commitment, and the capacity to learn combined with strong analytic and problem-solving skills the opportunity to shine. npower's graduate programme will introduce successful applicants to the many different facets of their business, and give them responsibility at an early stage within their chosen area of work.

npower are committed to attracting and retaining the best, so all their graduates receive an excellent pay and benefits package, including a competitive starting salary which is reviewed annually.

Which npower job do you want?

BUSINESS ANALYST

RISK ANALYST

BUSINESS MANAGER

ACCOUNTANT

ENGINEER

Everything we do at npower is fuelled by our unwavering hunger to be the best. We're looking for young graduates who have the same kind of drive as we do and are ready for the experience of their life.

There has never been a more exciting time to work in the world of energy generation and supply. npower need graduates to bring inspiration to the way we work; if you can bring enthusiasm, commitment, and the capacity to learn we'll give you the opportunity to shine. Our programme will introduce you to the many different facets of our business, and give you responsibility at an early stage within your chosen area of work.

If this sounds like the graduate job you want, visit our website today.

THE TIMES
TOP 50
WHERE WOMEN
WANT TO WORK
2008

visit www.brightergraduates.com

nucleargraduates

www.nucleargraduates.com

**Vacancies for around
60 graduates in 2010**

- Consulting
- Engineering
- General Management
- Logistics
- Purchasing
- Research & Development

Vacancies also available in Europe,
the USA and Asia.

Starting salary for 2010
£24,500

**Universities that
nucleargraduates
plans to visit in 2009-10**
Bath, Bristol, Cardiff,
Edinburgh, Hull,
Lancaster, Leeds,
Liverpool, Loughborough,
Manchester, Sheffield,
Southampton, Surrey
Please check with your university
careers service for details of events.

Application deadline
December 2009

Contact Details
✉ questions@
nucleargraduates.com
☎ 01925 802 212

Turn to page 224 now to request more
information or visit our new website at
www.top100graduateemployers.com

It's an exceptional time for the UK's nuclear industry. Existing
power stations are ready to be decommissioned. A new wave
of plants have been given the go ahead. Nuclear is back on
the agenda.

The factors behind this resurgence are complex – economic, ecological, political
and technological. But one thing is clear. The need for a new generation of
engineers, scientists and other professionals is greater than ever. That's why
the Nuclear Decommissioning Authority – a non departmental public body
– has brought leading businesses and organisations together to create a new
graduate programme, called nucleargraduates.

This two-year programme is the most comprehensive graduate scheme the
industry has ever seen. More than twenty different companies and governmental
bodies are backing it, including Sellafield, Rolls-Royce, BAE Systems, the
MoD and the Environment Agency. Of global importance, the scheme
includes placements across the UK and internationally. For instance, there are
opportunities to work in France, Sweden, India, the USA and Japan.

While the scheme is open to graduates from all disciplines, engineering
graduates are particularly encouraged to apply. Areas in which graduates
can specialise include Mechanical Engineering, Electrical Engineering and
Civil Engineering.

The nuclear sector can be divided into five key areas: decommissioning,
power generation, processing, defence and new build. The nucleargraduates
programme offers graduates the chance to experience work across these areas
– giving them unique experience and insight into the industry.

To find out more about this scheme, visit www.nucleargraduates.com

Who am I?

(Ⓧ) Oxfam

Be Humankind

www.oxfam.org.uk/interns

Vacancies for around 100 graduates in 2010

- ▮ Accountancy
- ▮ Finance
- ▮ General Management
- ▮ Human Resources
- ▮ IT
- ▮ Marketing
- ▮ Media
- ▮ Research & Development
- ▮ Retailing

Vacancies also available in Europe, the USA, Asia and elsewhere in the world.

Starting salary for 2010
£Voluntary

Universities that Oxfam plans to visit in 2009-10
Please check with your university careers service for details of events.

Application deadline
Year-round recruitment

Contact Details
✉ internship@oxfam.org.uk

Turn to page 224 now to request more information or visit our new website at www.top100graduateemployers.com

Swimming, cinema and socialising with friends...

Few organisations give graduates a genuine chance to make the world a better place. Oxfam does.

By harnessing the power of more than a million staff, volunteers and supporters, it's tackling the big issues. Like helping poor people prepare for the more frequent and severe natural disasters caused by climate change. Helping farmers adapt to the unpredictable weather so they don't go hungry. And pushing governments to come up with a fairer deal for everyone.

It's urgent, vital work. And it calls for passionate, committed, enthusiastic people. People who'll be vocal, take risks and challenge the norm – and who'll be ready to shoulder their share of responsibility. So graduates who join Oxfam's Voluntary Internship Scheme can forget tea rounds and shop runs. The scheme is planned round the precise needs of the organisation. Graduates can have a real impact – whether they volunteer part-time for three, six or 12 months.

The roles could be in Oxfam's Oxford Headquarters, a shop or a regional office. And they range from Deputy Shop Manager to placements in HR or Marketing. But whether graduates help to plan an event, manage a campaign or run a shop, they'll learn just how a major international Non Government Organisation works and enjoy an open culture. And although the work is unpaid, the scheme reimburses reasonable local travel and lunch expenses.

For graduates who want to save lives and campaign for lasting change, it's a fantastic way to build a CV that'll get noticed.

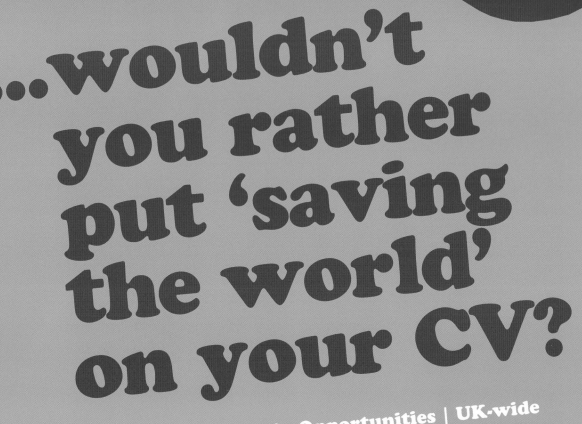

...wouldn't you rather put 'saving the world' on your CV?

Voluntary Internship Opportunities | UK-wide

Right wrongs right here. Take up an internship with an organisation that won't stand for climate change, poverty or injustice – and stand out. Swing into action at **www.oxfam.org.uk/interns**

 Oxfam works with others to overcome poverty and suffering.

 **Oxfam**

Be Humankind

COULD YOU?
POLICE

Vacancies for unlimited **graduates in 2010**

■ All sectors

Starting salary for 2010
£24,675
On completion of training,
plus excellent pension and benefits.

Universities that HPDS plans to visit in 2009-10
Please check with your university careers service for details of events.

Application deadline
Year-round recruitment

Contact Details
✉ hpds@npia.pnn.police.uk
☎ 020 7021 7070

Turn to page 224 now to request more information or visit our new website at www.top100graduateemployers.com

A career in the police offers an exciting mix of challenge and reward. Policing in today's police service involves reducing crime and the fear of crime, working in partnership with the public, supporting victims and witnesses whilst using the latest technology to assist with the detection and prevention of crime.

The challenges faced by police officers are often mental rather than physical, requiring an understanding of what makes people behave as they do, and to use that knowledge to develop strong policing skills. The modern police force offers a career with many opportunities to specialise in fields from intelligence to investigation.

There are great prospects to move up the career ladder into senior leadership positions. A Cambridge graduate, now a Chief Inspector, said of his decision to become a police officer that when he told his peers he was joining the police it was a conversation stopper, when he sees them now it is a conversation starter.

Graduates who have secured employment as a police officer with one of the forces in England, Wales or Northern Ireland are eligible to apply for the High Potential Development Scheme (HPDS). The HPDS aims to produce a cohort of officers who possess the operational credibility, management skills and strategic awareness to meet the challenges of senior police leadership. The HPDS is delivered in partnership with Warwick University and leads to a Masters Degree in Police Leadership.

Joining the police offers a starting salary of £24,675 p.a. on completion of initial training (additional allowances for officers in London and the South East) and an excellent pensions and benefits package.

For further information about the HPDS go to www.npia.police.uk/hpds

POLICE PLEASE CROSS

We Challenge You

Every single day in the police service is a challenge. We're looking for people of outstanding ability who meet those challenges.

Take the challenge of your lifetime, join the police.

PRICEWATERHOUSE COPERS

pwc.com/uk/careers/

Vacancies for around 1,000 graduates in 2010

- Accountancy
- Consulting
- Finance
- Law

Vacancies also available in Europe.

Starting salary for 2010
£Competitive

Universities that PricewaterhouseCoopers plans to visit in 2009-10

Aberdeen, Aston, Bath, Birmingham, Bristol, Cambridge, Cardiff, Durham, East Anglia, Edinburgh, Exeter, Glasgow, Heriot-Watt, Hull, Kent, Lancaster, Leeds, Liverpool, London, Loughborough, Manchester, Newcastle, Nottingham, Oxford, Plymouth, Reading, Sheffield, Southampton, St Andrews, Strathclyde, Surrey, Swansea, Warwick, York
Please check with your university careers service for details of events.

Application deadline
Year-round recruitment

Contact Details
☎ 0808 100 1500

Turn to page 224 now to request more information or visit our new website at www.top100graduateemployers.com

PricewaterhouseCoopers is a professional services powerhouse. They help organisations the world over measure their financial performance and improve the way they work. Clients range from public and private companies to governments and charities.

For graduates who are serious about a career in business, they don't believe anyone else could provide a better start. And they are proud to say that students agree, voting them number one in The Times Top 100 Graduate Employers survey for the last six years in a row.

Their people make them stand out as a firm. They choose the best and invest heavily in them. Graduates will benefit from training that helps them to gain breadth as well as depth of knowledge; support to gain a professional qualification and the chance to work in different teams and offices, experience different clients and projects, try out new roles and even sample other business areas. It will all help to develop along a path that fits personal aspirations as well as the ever-changing needs of their business. Bring them talent and commitment, and they will offer a competitive salary plus an innovative flexible benefits scheme.

They're after the very best. They need a 2:1 or above in any degree discipline, at least a 300 UCAS tariff or equivalent and a range of employability skills – including impact, drive, flexibility, curiosity, integrity and commercial awareness.

Find out more about their business, the recruitment process and how to apply at pwc.com/uk/careers/

INITIATIVE

IMPACT

VISION

DRIVE

TALENT

1NFORMED?

Assurance
Tax
Financial Advisory
Actuarial
Consulting
PwC Legal

Nationwide Opportunities Spring and Autumn 2010

Like to find out the facts? Then discover how much we can offer people with the right mix of employability skills. You'll learn from the experts who've made us a professional services powerhouse. You'll help tackle critical business issues and the most complex commercial challenges. And you'll soon see why we're the only employer to come first in the Times Top 100 Graduate Employers survey for six years running. Get to know an organisation that can make you even more knowledgeable, whatever direction you want to take.

Requirements:
2:1 in any degree discipline.
From 300 UCAS tariff or equivalent.

pwc.com/uk/careers/

Text: PwC to 85792 to visit our website on your mobile
(Texts charged at your standard network rate).

We value diversity in our people.

PRICEWATERHOUSECOOPERS

Vacancies for around 130 graduates in 2010

- Accountancy
- Engineering
- Finance
- Human Resources
- IT
- Logistics
- Manufacturing
- Marketing
- Purchasing
- Research & Development
- Sales

Vacancies also available in Europe.

Starting salary for 2010
£27,600

Universities that Procter & Gamble plans to visit in 2009-10

Aston, Bath, Birmingham, Cambridge, Dublin, Durham, Edinburgh, Lancaster, Leeds, Liverpool, London, Loughborough, Manchester, Nottingham, Oxford, Sheffield, St Andrews, Strathclyde, Warwick, York
Please check with your university careers service for details of events.

Application deadline
Year-round recruitment

Contact Details
✉ recunitedkingdm.im@pg.com

Turn to page 224 now to request more information or visit our new website at www.top100graduateemployers.com

Established 170 years ago, P&G is the most admired Household and Personal Goods company in the world (Fortune Magazine's Most Admired Companies 2008). It has one of the largest and strongest portfolios of trusted, quality brands, including Ariel, Always, Braun, Duracell, Gillette, Iams, Lenor, Max Factor, Olay, OralB, Pampers, Pantene, Pringles and Wella. Every day these brands touch the lives of more than three billion people around the world. 140,000 P&G people in 80 countries worldwide work to ensure P&G brands live up to their promise to make everyday life a little better.

P&G attracts and recruits the finest people in the world, because it grows and develops its senior managers within the organisation. This means new starters with P&G can expect a job with responsibility from day one and a career with a variety of challenging roles that develop and broaden their skills, together with the support of training and coaching to help them succeed.

P&G look for more than just good academic records from their applicants. They are looking for graduates who are smart and savvy, leaders who stand out from the crowd, who are able to get things done. They want to hear about achievements at work, in clubs, societies, voluntary and community activities and to see how graduates have stretched and challenged themselves and others. Most functions within the company welcome applicants from any degree discipline. Product Supply requires an engineering degree and R&D requires an engineering or science degree.

Graduates will find more details about what P&G look for, their selection process and the jobs available by going to their website at www.pgcareers.com

We'll help you find your feet and then

GROW AND GROW...

At P&G, we hire the person, not the position, so we will do all we can to quickly help you become a success.

We guarantee you real responsibility from day one, so you'll immediately play your part in creating best-value products that meet the ever changing needs of our consumers and have a direct impact on a global, $80 billion business.

With nearly 300 of the world's most trusted brands to our name and exciting projects across every area of our business, you can be sure P&G will give you plenty of room for growth.

**For information visit
*www.PGcareers.com***

A NEW CHALLENGE EVERY DAY.™
Daily. Globally. Personally. Professionally.

QinetiQ

Vacancies for around 150 graduates in 2010

- Engineering
- Finance
- Research & Development

Starting salary for 2010
£24,000

Universities that QinetiQ plans to visit in 2009-10

Bath, Birmingham, Bristol, Cardiff, Exeter, Glasgow, Liverpool, London, Loughborough, Manchester, Nottingham, Oxford, Sheffield, St Andrews, Strathclyde, Warwick, York
Please check with your university careers service for details of events.

Application deadline
31st December 2009

Contact Details
Turn to page 224 now to request more information or visit our new website at www.top100graduateemployers.com

WHERE IDEAS BECOME REALITY

People who are full of brilliant ideas owe it to themselves, and everyone else, to ensure that they build their careers with a company that will help those ideas become reality. A company like QinetiQ, who'll provide the amazing colleagues, world class technology, unique research facilities and unstinting support to turn inspired inklings into incredible products that solve seemingly impossible problems.

QinetiQ is a world-renowned defence, technology and security company seeking 150 extraordinary new science, engineering and technology graduates a year. They look for proactive, analytical, forward-thinking people with commercial instinct, questioning minds and passion.

Inspired by pioneering research, QinetiQ delivers commercial value from science on the widest possible range of projects. So they offer a similarly broad range of careers covering operational analysis, scientific research, development, test and evaluation and project management – in fields ranging from media to healthcare, aerospace to security and telecoms to transport. All roles combine a good salary and benefits package with real quality of life – the chance to do fascinating work in a pleasant environment.

In addition to the core graduate development programme, there is the potential to attend conferences, undertake secondments and, where appropriate, gain support for further qualifications, such as Chartered status, an MSc, or PhD. Whether graduates want to follow a technical path or take a business or project management route, they'll be surrounded by opportunities. But it will be up to the individual to make the most of them.

QinetiQ people are open, imaginative and agile enough to blend all kinds of inspiration. Their heads are a constant whirl of influences, issues and inklings. They brim over with bubbling, frothy genius and we give them the colleagues, technology, facilities and support to turn hair-brained hunches into actual, bona fide, whirring, buzzing, chugging solutions. Incredible, ground-breaking solutions to seemingly impossible problems. Inspiration is nothing without consummation. If you're a science, engineering or technology graduate who's full of ideas and driven enough to see them through, apply online at www.QinetiQgraduates.co.uk/tt

QinetiQ

Rolls-Royce

www.rolls-royce.com/university

**Vacancies for around
210 graduates in 2010**

- Engineering
- Finance
- General Management
- Human Resources
- Logistics
- Manufacturing
- Purchasing
- Research & Development
- Sales

Vacancies also available in Europe,
the USA and Asia.

Starting salary in 2009
£25,500-£28,000

**Universities Rolls-Royce
plans to visit in 2009-10**

Bath, Birmingham, Bristol,
Cambridge, City, Durham,
Edinburgh, London,
Loughborough, Manchester,
Nottingham, Oxford,
Sheffield, Southampton,
Strathclyde, Warwick
Please check with your university
careers service for details of events.

Application deadline
Year-round recruitment

Contact Details
✉ HRSharedServiceCentre@
rolls-royce.com
☎ 01332 333 333

Turn to page 224 now to request more
information or visit our new website at
www.top100graduateemployers.com

Graduates are proud to work for Rolls-Royce, as they contribute to a variety of exciting projects that power the world.

As an engineering company renowned for its technological excellence, Rolls-Royce is a global market leader in the highly competitive civil aerospace, defence aerospace, marine and energy sectors, developing innovative solutions to address today's burning issues. Issues such as how to meet the world's demand for air travel, while reducing its effect on the environment.

Graduates face some of the most challenging business scenarios imaginable. It's a highly competitive world that requires the best supply chain, the strongest finance operations, the most creative deal-makers, the best-organised project managers, the greatest customer focus and the finest engineers. There are two graduate programmes on offer. The Professional Excellence Programme enables graduates to become a recognised expert in a particular field. The Leadership Development Programme focuses on developing leadership skills within a function.

These programmes challenge, stretch and enthuse graduates from a range of backgrounds. Tailored to meet the graduates' individual needs, they enable them to perform to their full potential through a combination of job experience, formal training, project work and a variety of other activities.

With 38,000 employees around the world, the company aims to make a positive contribution to the communities they operate in. This means graduates enjoy the chance to work closely with colleagues in a variety of countries and are encouraged to get involved in a range of community-based projects.

Power. Innovation. Progress.

Graduate programmes in: Engineering, Commercial, Customer Management, Finance, HR, Manufacturing Leadership, Project Management, Purchasing, Supply Chain

Graduate opportunities

As one of the best known and most respected names in engineering, we have built success on a century's worth of excellence and innovation. But with £56bn worth of orders on our books, an annual R&D spend of £900m, and a firm commitment to recruit more graduates than we've ever done before, we firmly believe our best years are ahead of us.

Give your career some forward momentum. Join a global business providing power systems for use on land, at sea & in the air.
Visit www.rolls-royce.com/university

Trusted to deliver excellence

www.rolls-royce.com

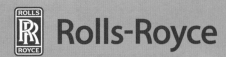

Rolls-Royce

The Royal Bank of Scotland Group

www.makeitrbs.com

Vacancies for around 400+ graduates in 2010

- Accountancy
- Finance
- General Management
- Investment Banking
- IT
- Marketing
- Purchasing
- Retailing
- Sales

Vacancies also available in Europe, the USA, Asia and elsewhere in the world.

Starting salary for 2010
£Competitive
Plus benefit funding.

Universities that The Royal Bank of Scotland Group plans to visit in 2009-10

Aston, Bath, Birmingham, Bristol, Cambridge, City, Durham, Edinburgh, Exeter, Glasgow, Heriot-Watt, Lancaster, Leeds, London, Loughborough, Manchester, Newcastle, Nottingham, Oxford, Sheffield, Southampton, St Andrews, Strathclyde, Warwick
Please check with your university careers service for details of events.

Application deadline
Varies by function
See website for full details.

Contact Details
Turn to page 224 now to request more information or visit our new website at www.top100graduateemployers.com

Talented people and particularly graduates are essential to the future of The Royal Bank of Scotland Group. To say RBS has had its challenges is an understatement, however, they know what went wrong, are taking decisive action to fix problems, and have a new strategic plan in place to regain strength.

RBS is looking to the future, and for graduates this exciting period of change presents an unprecedented opportunity to be part of the solution. Those who join now will have an important part to play in redefining the organisation in the months and years to come. With that in mind, there's never been a more exciting time to join.

Few organisations can offer the choice of careers graduates will discover at RBS. The variety of options available across the RBS business is a match for the very best graduate talent.

Programmes offered include: Business & Commercial Banking; Corporate Banking; GBM Operations; GBM Technology; Global Banking & Markets; Global Restructuring Group; Global Transaction Services; Group Manufacturing Leadership; Group Sourcing & Vendor Management; Group Technology Services; Internships and placements; Marketing; Private Banking; RBS Finance; RBS Insurance; RBS Risk; Retail Business Leadership and Ulster Bank Group – Corporate Markets.

Graduates will need a 2:1 or 2:2 depending on programme. Support will be provided via a network of buddies and mentors as well as a first class development programme. They will also have the opportunity to continue studying for professional qualifications.

LOOKINGFORWARD

GRADUATE CAREERS

UK, Europe, USA and Asia

It's now time to look to the future. For ambitious and forward-thinking graduates this exciting period of change presents an opportunity to influence from day one and shape the future of RBS. With over 20 graduate and internship programmes in everything from Global Banking & Markets, Finance and Retail Business Leadership to Technology, Marketing and Sourcing & Vendor Management there's something for everyone, whatever degree discipline and career aspiration.

Visit **www.makeitrbs.com** for more information and to apply.

royalnavy.mod.uk/careers

Vacancies also available elsewhere in the world.

Starting salary for 2010
£29,006

Universities that the Royal Navy plans to visit in 2009-10
Aberdeen, Bath, Bristol, Brunel, Cardiff, Dundee, Durham, East Anglia, Edinburgh, Exeter, Heriot-Watt, Leeds, Loughborough, Stirling, Surrey
Please check with your university careers service for details of events.

Application deadline
Year-round recruitment

Contact Details
☎ 08456 07 55 55
Turn to page 224 now to request more information or visit our new website at www.top100graduateemployers.com

A life at sea has always attracted those with a taste for travel and adventure. But in today's unpredictable job market, there are plenty of other reasons for graduates and final-year students to consider a career with the Royal Navy.

The Royal Navy is, first and foremost, a fighting force, serving alongside Britain's allies in conflicts around the world. It also protects UK ports, fishing grounds and merchant ships and helps combat international smuggling, terrorism and piracy. Increasingly, its 35,000 personnel are involved in humanitarian and relief missions, where their skills, discipline and resourcefulness make a real difference to people's lives.

Graduates are able to join the Royal Navy as Officers – the senior management team in the various branches, which range from Engineering and Warfare to Medical, the Fleet Air Arm and Logistics. Starting salaries of at least £29,006 compare well with those in industry, with joining bonuses also on offer in some branches. Those wanting to join the Royal Navy as an Engineer Officer can receive a £12,000 joining bonus (minus tax). What's more, the Royal Navy can offer the security of a full career of 18 years, with the potential to extend.

The opportunities for early responsibility, career development, sport, recreation and travel exceed any in civilian life. With its global reach and responsibilities, the Royal Navy still offers the chance to see the world, while pursuing a challenging, varied and fulfilling career.

The Royal Navy recruits year-round; current information on the many jobs available can be found at royalnavy.mod.uk/careers

ROYAL NAVY ENGINEER OFFICER SUBMARINER:
THERE'S MORE BENEATH THE SURFACE

£5,000 SUBMARINER QUALIFYING BONUS*
£12,000 ENGINEER JOINING BONUS*
£29,006-£87,655** PA
COVERT OPERATIONS
ELITE TRAINING
6 WEEKS' PAID HOLIDAY

If all those facts aren't surprising enough, here's a few more. Whether it's working with our most advanced weapons or providing undersea protection for our Surface Fleet, every role on board makes a real difference. The team spirit is second to none and you'll find that each task is both varied and exciting.

So what's the real secret weapon on board? It's the Engineer Officers who are at the heart of keeping these advanced submarines running smoothly and silently. By looking after the weapon, sensor, communication, nuclear, mechanical and life-support systems on board, they're essential to ensuring the success of each and every mission.

If you want more than just a job, join the Royal Navy and live a life without limits.

Join the Royal Navy
royalnavy.mod.uk/careers
or call 08456 07 55 55

ROYAL NAVY
LIFE WITHOUT LIMITS

Sainsbury's

Vacancies for around 85 graduates in 2010

- Finance
- General Management
- Human Resources
- IT
- Logistics
- Marketing
- Purchasing
- Retailing

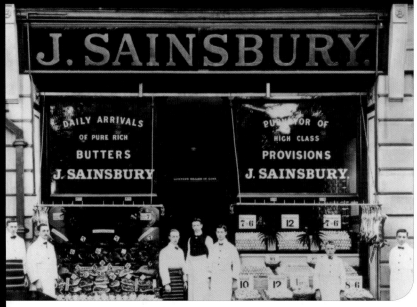

Starting salary for 2010
£23,000-£25,000
Dependant on scheme.

Universities Sainsbury's plans to visit in 2009-10
Bath, Birmingham, Bristol, Cardiff, Durham, Exeter, Lancaster, Leeds, London, Loughborough, Manchester, Newcastle, Northumbria, Nottingham, Reading, Sheffield, Southampton, Strathclyde, Warwick, York
Please check with your university careers service for details of events.

Application deadline
31st December 2009

Contact Details
☎ 0845 603 6290
Turn to page 224 now to request more information or visit our new website at www.top100graduateemployers.com

Sainsbury's is more than just a food retailer; it is a diverse business that enjoys universal appeal and a rich 140 year heritage. As one of the top retailers in the FTSE 100 there are a number of different ways for graduates to get involved. It is looking for exceptional graduates that will help bring fresh talent and ideas to the business and who are hungry to play a part of its continued success.

Despite the turbulent time in the retail sector over the last 12 months Sainsbury's has gone from strength to strength. Its trusted brand and efforts to adjust its offer to meet the changing needs of customers mean Sainsbury's has outperformed many of its rivals. This success means over 18.5 million Customers now visit Sainsbury's each week with profits up 11% compared to last year. Sainsbury's has now enjoyed four years of like-for-like sales growth, an achievement in any economic climate.

But don't just take Sainsbury's word for it – visit www.j-sainsbury.co.uk for more details on its performance in the last 12 months and exciting plans for the future.

Sainsbury's has a long-term commitment to recruiting high-calibre graduates and believes graduates are integral to the future success of its business.

For more information on the breadth of opportunities available, please visit www.sainsburys.co.uk/graduates. Exceptional graduates, with at least a 2:1 degree should apply now as places are going fast.

The economy is challenging.
True.

Lots of companies aren't even taking any graduates on.
Also true.

So why do graduates still matter so much to Sainsbury's?

Even in this tough climate our sector is doing really well. And in fact, we're outperforming it. Customer numbers are up and so are our sales with graduates in every area of our business making a huge contribution. As they always have done.

That's why we're still seriously interested in talented graduates joining us.

You can get the full picture at
www.sainsburys.co.uk/graduates

Graduate opportunities 2009/10

WHAT WILL THE WORLD BE LIKE IN 2050?

Vacancies for around 100 graduates in 2010

- Engineering
- Finance
- Human Resources
- IT
- Marketing
- Sales

Vacancies also available in Europe.

Starting salary for 2010
£31,150
Plus bonuses, pension and benefits.

Universities that Shell plans to visit in 2009-10
Aberdeen, Bath, Birmingham, Bristol, Cambridge, Durham, Edinburgh, Heriot-Watt, Leeds, London, Loughborough, Manchester, Nottingham, Oxford, Sheffield, Strathclyde, Warwick
Please check with your university careers service for details of events.

Application deadline
Year-round recruitment

Contact Details
✉ graduates@shell.com
☎ 0845 600 1819
Turn to page 224 now to request more information or visit our new website at www.top100graduateemployers.com

Whatever new technology the future holds, the world will need plenty of energy to power it and Shell is working on all sorts of ideas to meet the growing demand. With a large number of opportunities in a wide range of commercial and technical roles, they need ambitious graduates to help them tackle the energy challenge.

While a strong academic background is important to Shell, it's not the main consideration. To enable people to thrive in a dynamic and innovative organisation such as Shell, the selection processes are designed to assess the qualities of Capacity, Achievement and Relationship (CAR). Graduates will have the ability to absorb information, analyse problems, make objective decisions and come up with innovative ideas. They will also be enthusiastic and confident, and capable of working in a diverse team. With this in mind, successful applicants display these qualities throughout the process.

Everyone who works for Shell thrives on stimulation and challenge. It offers superb training, support and career choices, and develop potential by teaming all graduates with some of the most accomplished problem solvers in the business.

There are three ways to get a job with Shell: The Gourami Business Challenge, Shell Recruitment Day, or Paid Student Internship, and all its graduates chose which route works best for them. Whichever path they take, a comprehensive onboarding programme helps them settle into their new role, and Shell's early career development programme ensures they get off to a flying start. Think further. Visit www.shell.co.uk/careers

TECHNICAL & COMMERCIAL CAREERS
NELLY JOINED SHELL IN 2008

"I wanted to work for Shell because of the international opportunities I knew they would offer me. There's a culture here where people feel responsible and concerned not just for their work, but also for other people around them. There's always a chance of either specialising in a field or moving around different business areas where I can learn and develop as much as possible."

So if you want to achieve more in a technical or commercial career, get together with Shell at **www.shell.co.uk/careers** and quote reference **GGY311S** when applying.

Shell is an equal opportunity employer.

Think further. Visit www.shell.co.uk/careers

GREAT MINDS DON'T THINK ALIKE

SIEMENS

www.siemens.co.uk/grad

Vacancies for around 30-40 graduates in 2010

- Engineering
- Finance
- General Management
- IT

Starting salary for 2010
£Competitive

Universities that Siemens plans to visit in 2009-10
Loughborough, Manchester, Newcastle, Nottingham Sheffield, Southampton, Warwick
Please check with your university careers service for details of events.

Application deadline
Year-round recruitment

Contact Details
✉ graduate.recruitment.cp.gb@ siemens.com
☎ 01276 690 204

Turn to page 224 now to request more information or visit our new website at www.top100graduateemployers.com

How can a sustainable future be created and a growing population be supported? How can growing energy demands be balanced with the needs of the planet? Big questions demand big answers. And that's what drives everyone at Siemens, one of the world's largest engineering companies.

From healthcare, to industry to energy and the environment, Siemens is working hard to answer the big questions of our time. So graduates looking for a career where they'll be supported, trained and challenged, should join one of their structured two-year Graduate Development Programmes.

As a company, Siemens is proud of its continuous learning environment and its unswerving commitment to innovation. Graduates will see both in action, whether they want to develop a career in Engineering, IT or Business.

Take Business. Successful ones don't run themselves. They take a lot of planning, organising and hard work. Graduates will play an important part in making the Siemens business function, whether they want to develop their career in HR, Finance, Project and Operations Management, or Sales.

The range of Engineering careers on offer within Siemens are as diverse as their industry sectors and projects. From wind power to transportation, broadcast technology to building services they offer challenging careers for thought-leaders in the sector.

Then there's IT. With a strong track record in delivering some of the UK's most advanced and exciting IT projects, Siemens enjoys long term relationships with a number of the best known names in business and public services provision in the UK. Working across the consult, design, build and operate spectrum, they offer an exciting career path for IT graduates looking to pursue a career in the industry.

Final exams are on Monday.
What do we do after that?

**Vacancies for around
50 graduates in 2010**

- Accountancy
- General Management
- IT
- Logistics
- Marketing

Starting salary for 2010
£22,000-£26,000+

**Universities that Sky
plans to visit in 2009-10**

Bath, Birmingham,
Cambridge, Durham,
Edinburgh, Glasgow,
Heriot-Watt, London,
Manchester, Nottingham,
Oxford, Oxford Brookes,
Strathclyde, Warwick, York
Please check with your university
careers service for details of events.

Application deadline
See website for full details.

Contact Details
Turn to page 224 now to request more
information or visit our new website at
www.top100graduateemployers.com

Sky Future Talent

We've created the natural environment
for talented graduates looking for the
brightest of futures.

One of the world's leading entertainment companies, with over
17 million viewers in more than nine million households, Sky
employ cutting edge technology to create the ultimate customer
experience – from online and mobile to High Definition and their
latest experiments with 3DTV in the home via the increasingly
popular Sky+ box.

The business is no less innovative in its approach to sustainability, and
is working hard to make its operations as environmentally friendly as
possible. In fact, in 2006, Sky became the world's first CarbonNeutral®
media company.

Sky have four highly regarded graduate development programmes, in
Marketing, Finance, Technology and Contact Centre & Supply Chain.
All offer unparalleled exposure to the workings of a FTSE top 30 business,
plus funding to gain a recognised professional qualification and the
opportunity to be involved in some of Sky's most interesting and
exciting projects.

As learning environments go, theirs is certainly a progressive one. As well
as being fast moving, stimulating and supportive. The ideal place for
ambitious graduates to be part of something big, while being very much
encouraged to be themselves. And confident communicators who believe
they've the potential to go far can look forward to early responsibility and
the chance to develop their talents through work that is both challenging
and meaningful.

For more information go to www.workforsky.com

SLAUGHTER AND MAY

Vacancies for around 95 graduates in 2010
For training contracts starting in 2012

 Law

Starting salary for 2010
£38,000

Universities that Slaughter and May plans to visit in 2009-10
Birmingham, Bristol, Cambridge, Durham, Edinburgh, Leeds, London, Manchester, Nottingham, Oxford, Warwick
Please check with your university careers service for details of events.

Application deadline
Year-round recruitment

Contact Details
✉ trainee.recruit@ slaughterandmay.com

Turn to page 224 now to request more information or visit our new website at www.top100graduateemployers.com

Slaughter and May is a leading international law firm whose principal areas of practice are in the fields of corporate, commercial and financing law.

The firm's clients range from the world's leading multinationals to venture capital start-ups. They include public and private companies, governments and non-governmental organisations, commercial and investment banks. The lawyers devise solutions for complex, often transnational, problems and advise some of the world's brightest business minds.

Their overseas offices and close working relationships with leading independent law firms in other jurisdictions mean there are opportunities to work in places such as Auckland, Brussels, Berlin, Copenhagen, Düsseldorf, Frankfurt, Helsinki, Hong Kong, Luxembourg, Madrid, Milan, New York, Oslo, Paris, Prague, Rome, Singapore, Stockholm, Sydney and Tokyo.

Approximately 95 training contracts are available per year for trainee solicitors. Slaughter and May also offers work experience schemes at Christmas, Easter and during the summer for those considering a career in law.

Following Law School, there is a two year training period during which time trainee solicitors gain experience of a broad cross-section of the firm's practice by taking an active part in the work of four or five groups, sharing an office with a partner or experienced associate. In addition, Slaughter and May offers an extensive training programme of lectures, seminars and courses with discussion groups covering general and specialised legal topics.

Applications from candidates of good 2.1 ability from any discipline are considered. Please visit the website for further information.

Teach First
LEARNING TO LEAD

Vacancies for around 700 graduates in 2010

■ All Sectors

Starting salary for 2010
£Competitive

Universities Teach First plans to visit in 2009-10

Aston, Bath, Birmingham, Bristol, Brunel, Cambridge, Cardiff, City, Durham, Edinburgh, Essex, Exeter, Glasgow, Lancaster, Leeds, Leicester, Liverpool, London, Loughborough, Manchester, Newcastle, Nottingham, Nottingham Trent, Oxford, Sheffield, Southampton, St Andrews, Surrey, Sussex, Warwick, York

Please check with your university careers service for details of events.

Application deadline
2nd April 2010

Apply by 5th December 2009 for best choice of subjects.

Contact Details

✉ faq@teachfirst.org.uk

☎ 020 7517 2734

Turn to page 224 now to request more information or visit our new website at www.top100graduateemployers.com

It's time to make a difference – to invest in changing lives and achieving something lasting. Energy, intelligence and creativity can transform the futures of students and drive up standards in challenging schools around the UK.

Teach First's two-year programme provides the training and support to enable high-calibre graduates to make a real impact. At the same time it provides an opportunity to dramatically enhance their own career potential and become part of a movement that is effecting profound change across the UK.

And while graduates are transforming the lives of young people in schools around the country, Teach First helps them to maximise their own potential. With high-quality training – leading to the achievement of Qualified Teacher Status – leadership development and supportive coaching and ongoing alumni programmes, Teach First provides a strong platform of skills and experience to take forward into any future management career. That's why over 80 companies, government agencies and public bodies back Teach First to develop top talent for the future.

Put simply, graduates who can engage, manage and stimulate a class of under-performing teenagers can handle pretty well any situation in any business. Few other options offer the same degree of genuine responsibility so early. And rarely, if ever, will graduates have the opportunity to make such a direct and important difference.

Teach First is a chance to join in, and to stand out. And when it offers so much, the real question is why not Teach First?

BETH
LOMAX
BATH

ROSHAN
NILAWEERA
BRISTOL

LAURA
HOUSE
CAMBRIDGE

BEN
BARTLETT
EDINBURGH

Join in, stand out.

f you could really make a difference, would you?
f you could change children's lives, would you?
f you could inspire and lead them to achieve their potential, would you?

And if doing all this changed your own future too, the real question is why wouldn't you?

Teach **First**

LEARNING TO LEAD

www.teachfirst.org.uk

TESCO

www.tesco-graduates.com

Vacancies for around 200 graduates in 2010

- Accountancy
- Consulting
- Engineering
- Finance
- General Management
- Human Resources
- IT
- Logistics
- Marketing
- Purchasing
- Retailing

Starting salary for 2010
£Competitive

Universities that Tesco plans to visit in 2009-10
Cambridge, Durham, London, Loughborough, Manchester, Nottingham Trent, Oxford, Reading
Please check with your university careers service for details of events.

Application deadline
See website for full details.

Contact Details
✉ graduate.recruitment@ uk.tesco.com

Turn to page 224 now to request more information or visit our new website at www.top100graduateemployers.com

Tesco is best known as the UK's number one retailer – a worldwide brand with a £59.4billion turnover. As The Times Graduate Employer of Choice 2008 for General Management, Tesco are also recognised for their fantastic graduate opportunities.

But there's a lot more to Tesco. Something people may not realise is they're a pioneer in greener retailing: they have reduced carrier bag usage by three billion and are rated the 15th greenest company in the UK. What's more, Tesco's greenest store ever opened this year in Manchester, with a 70% lower carbon footprint than typical stores.

For graduates, this innovation means they'll be joining a forward-thinking company that takes corporate social responsibility seriously – much like the development of their graduates. In fact, Tesco offers a total of 17 diverse graduate programmes that each provide huge scope for progression. Whether graduates want to begin their career in, to name a few, property, customer analysis, stores or distribution, Tesco's breadth of graduate programmes has it covered.

Depending on the area they join, graduates get involved in anything from sourcing products, to negotiating prices with suppliers, and predicting sales forecasts for acquiring land. Within three to five years, graduates can even be running their own store. In other words, Tesco's structured fast-track programmes offer outstanding rewards and development.

Tesco looks for ambitious graduates from any discipline who have the drive to succeed and understand the importance of delivering for the customer, whatever part of the business they work in.

Success.   Sustained.

With 470,000 staff, stores in 14 countries and a total sales increase
of over 50% during the past 5 years, it would be difficult to miss our
business growth. Even our broccoli sales now weigh in at 450 tonnes
a week in the UK.

But what may have passed you by is our growth as a green and sustainable
business too. From getting our Tesco train on track delivering supplies by
rail, to supporting farmers by buying localchoice milk, we're cutting our CO_2
emissions more and more each day. We're even saving 20,000 tonnes of
cardboard by delivering products in reusable plastic trays. Come and help
us sustain our success, visit **www.tesco-graduates.com**

Graduate Programmes:

Buying	Property (Includes: Construction
Corporate Affairs	& Development , Design,
Corporate Marketing	Engineering and Product
Customer Analysis	Display & Space Management)
Distribution Management	Site Research
Finance	Store Management
Human Resources	Supply Chain
Merchandising	Technology Leadership
Product Technology	Tesco.com
	Tesco Telecoms
	UK Support Office

www.tesco-graduates.com

Tesco is an equal opportunities employer.

TESCO | *Every little helps*

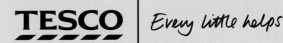

Transport for London

tfl.gov.uk/tt100

Vacancies for around 100 graduates in 2010

- Accountancy
- Engineering
- Finance
- General Management
- Human Resources
- IT
- Logistics
- Purchasing

Starting salary for 2010
c.£25,000

Universities that Transport for London plans to visit in 2009-10
Bath, Bristol, Brunel, Cambridge, City, Leeds, London, Nottingham, Oxford, Sheffield, Southampton, Warwick
Please check with your university careers service for details of events.

Application deadline
Varies by function
See website for full details.

Contact Details
✉ questions@tflgraduates.co.uk
☎ 0870 1267549
Turn to page 224 now to request more information or visit our new website at www.top100graduateemployers.com

London
is a roost
for every
bird.
Benjamin Disraeli

Transport for London (TfL) has a huge part to play in making London what it is. The Tube, the trains, the buses, the river, the roads, the trams, the DLR, the taxis, the cycle lanes – TfL is responsible for virtually every mode of transport in the city.

The graduates that join TfL will enjoy just as much impact on the Capital. They could explore engineering or finance; procurement or management; transport planning or project management; quantity surveying or IM.

They might find themselves running an entire Underground station; examining how London's transport infrastructure fits together; or putting a project into place that could radically change how people travel across the city. TfL certainly doesn't shy away from giving their graduates heavy responsibility, very early on.

In fact, there's a great deal graduates could be influencing. Right now, TfL is in the midst of one of the greatest periods of investment in its history. Low-carbon taxis are being introduced. Buses are being redesigned. A cycling revolution is underway. The Tube is being comprehensively upgraded. New railways are being created. Plus, of course, the 2012 Games are on their way.

Whichever opportunity graduates choose, and whatever they turn their talent to, they can expect support, training and responsibility worthy of one of London's largest employers. These are unique opportunities for people with the flair, potential and personality to make a vital contribution to one of the world's greatest cities.

The world is but a canvas to the imagination.

Henry David Thoreau

Leave your mark on London – become a TfL graduate.

We want to be as diverse as the city we represent and welcome applications from everyone regardless of age, gender, ethnicity, sexual orientation, faith or disability.

tfl.gov.uk/tt100

MAYOR OF LONDON

Transport for London

Vacancies for around 150 graduates in 2010

- Accountancy
- Finance
- Human Resources
- Investment Banking
- IT

Vacancies also available in Europe.

Starting salary for 2010
£Competitive

Universities that UBS plans to visit in 2009-10
Please check with your university careers service for details of events.

Application deadline
1st November 2009

Contact Details
✉ SH-UBS-CampusRecruiting@ubs.com
Turn to page 224 now to request more information or visit our new website at www.top100graduateemployers.com

Headquartered in Zurich and Basel, Switzerland, UBS is one of the world's leading financial firms. UBS serves a discerning, international client base with wealth management, investment banking and asset management businesses. In Switzerland, they are the market leader in retail and commercial banking.

UBS is present in all major financial centres worldwide. They have offices in over 50 countries, with about 38% of the employees working in the Americas, 34% in Switzerland, 15% in the rest of Europe and 13% in Asia Pacific.

UBS believes the key to achieving growth and change is attracting the most talented, qualified and motivated people and giving them every opportunity to succeed. The environment is supportive, but the pace is quick. Graduates at UBS are asked to use their judgement every day to make important decisions that impact themselves, their teams and clients.

In return for their hard work UBS offers a rewarding career where graduates can develop and grow. UBS's global reach, collaborative culture and world-class graduate training program are just some of the factors that make UBS an excellent place to work.

UBS looks for applications from all degree disciplines. Academic credentials are important, but equally important are demonstrable skills such as problem analysis, judgement and decision making, planning and organising, communication, drive and commitment, teamwork and innovation. In addition, they look for students with strong technical skills and language skills.

Together we...

turn differences into strengths.

We are a unique global team. Because at UBS, you can work in an international environment with people from all walks of life. The diversity of our workforce inspires us to be more creative and innovative. Not just in the way we work, but in our approach to the people who really matter: our clients. You will work alongside exceptional managers who understand the importance of each individual as part of a team. Join one of the world's leading financial firms to make all our differences our greatest strength.

It starts with you: www.ubs.com/graduates

UBS is an Equal Opportunity Employer. We respect and seek to empower each individual and the diverse cultures, perspectives, skills and experiences within our workforce.

Wealth Management | Global Asset Management | Investment Bank

You & Us

 UBS

Unilever

Vacancies for around 40 graduates in 2010

- Engineering
- Finance
- Human Resources
- IT
- Marketing
- Research & Development
- Sales

Starting salary for 2010
£26,500
Plus benefits.

Universities that Unilever plans to visit in 2009-10
Bath, Birmingham, Bristol, Durham, Edinburgh, Lancaster, Leeds, Liverpool, London, Loughborough, Manchester, Nottingham, Oxford, Sheffield, Warwick
Please check with your university careers service for details of events.

Application deadline
See website for full details.

Contact Details
✉ enquiry@
unilevergraduates.com
☎ 0870 154 3550

Turn to page 224 now to request more information or visit our new website at www.top100graduateemployers.com

Unilever is a leading consumer goods company, making and marketing products in the foods, home and personal care sectors across the world.

In fact over half the families in the world use brands such as Dove, Magnum, Knorr, Persil and Lynx every day. Unilever's mission is to add vitality to life – by helping people feel good, look good and get more out of life. Behind every successful brand lie a number of complex challenges, in all areas of the business: these are what graduates at Unilever will tackle.

Unilever's Future Leaders Programme is designed to help graduates reach senior management. Graduates join a specific function in Unilever, where they have a real job with key deliverables and responsibilities from the outset. Generally, the scheme includes four placements in various locations within two years therefore flexibility is essential to achieve the breadth of experience required. There is excellent training covering leadership development, general business and professional skills. Full support is offered to gain Chartered status or relevant professional qualifications, such as CIMA, IMechE, IChemE and IEE.

Unilever wants people with the potential to lead its business. To do this, graduates need to be passionate about business, inspired by profit, competition and customer satisfaction, as well as have the ability to behave with integrity showing both ambition and entrepreneurial spirit. Unilever's high quality training programmes help graduates develop the expertise and personal qualities they need in order to achieve their career goals. They offer a vast range of opportunities that just have to be taken.

WANT TO DO WELL BY DOING GOOD

It's part of our DNA. Unilever is a business with incredible global influence. And we use that to do world-changing work, helping strengthen the communities who support our success. We choose to persuade our palm oil suppliers not to destroy the rainforest. We develop soaps that require less water to use. We decided to source our tea sustainably – and to ask the Rainforest Alliance to certify our plantations. You want to do world-changing work? Then come and do it with a company that genuinely has the power to change how consumerism operates.

Join Unilever as a graduate and have a real job with real responsibility from day one. If you succeed in the programme, after two years you will have your first management position. How's that for a chance to do well? With opportunities in Marketing, Supply Chain, Research & Development, Customer Development, IT, HR and Financial Management, there's bound to be something to match your degree and interests. Find out more and apply via our website.

Could it be **U** Unilever

WANT MORE VISIT UNILEVER.CO.UK/CAREERS

WPP

www.wpp.com

Vacancies for around 1-10 graduates in 2010

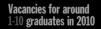

Marketing

Media

Vacancies also available in Europe, the USA, Asia and elsewhere in the world.

Starting salary for 2010
£Competitive

Universities that WPP plans to visit in 2009-10
Bristol, Cambridge, Edinburgh, London, Nottingham, Oxford, Warwick
Please check with your university careers service for details of events.

Application deadline
17th November 2009

Contact Details
✉ hmiller@wpp.com
☎ 020 7408 2204

Turn to page 224 now to request more information or visit our new website at www.top100graduateemployers.com

WPP is one of the world's leading communications services groups, made up of leading companies in advertising; media investment management; information, insight & consultancy; public relations & public affairs; branding & identity; healthcare communications; direct, digital, promotion & relationship marketing; and specialist communications.

WPP companies provide communications services to clients worldwide including more than 345 of the Fortune Global 500, 29 of the Dow Jones 30, half of the NASDAQ 100 and 33 of the Fortune e-50. Collectively, WPP employs 135,000 people (including associates) in almost 2,400 offices in 107 countries.

WPP Marketing Fellowships, which develop high-calibre management talent with experience across a range of marketing disciplines, will be awarded to applicants who are intellectually curious and motivated by the prospect of delivering high-quality communications services to their clients. All applicants should have completed an undergraduate degree (class 2:1 or above) or equivalent. Those selected will work in a number of WPP companies and across different marketing disciplines.

WPP is offering several three-year Fellowships – a unique multi-disciplinary experience, competitive remuneration and excellent long term career prospects within WPP. It wants people who are committed to marketing, who take a rigorous and creative approach to problem-solving, who are intellectually curious and will function well in a flexible, loosely structured work environment.

Each year of the Fellowship is spent working in a WPP sponsoring company and a personal mentor is assigned to provide overall career guidance. Each rotation is chosen on the basis of the individual's interests and the Group's needs.

WPP

Marketing Fellowships 2010

Ambidextrous brains required

WPP is one of the world's leading communications services groups. Major brands include JWT, Ogilvy & Mather Worldwide, Y&R, Grey, United, Mindshare, Mediaedge:cia, MediaCom, Millward Brown, Kantar Media, OgilvyOne Worldwide, Wunderman, OgilvyAction, Hill & Knowlton, Ogilvy Public Relations Worldwide, Burson-Marsteller, Cohn & Wolfe, CommonHealth, Sudler & Hennessey, TNS, Ogilvy Healthworld, ghg, The Brand Union, Landor, Fitch and G2 among others.

Their specialist skills include Advertising; Media Investment Management; Information, Insight & Consultancy; Public Relations & Public Affairs; Branding & Identity; Healthcare Communications; Direct, Digital,

Promotion & Relationship Marketing; and Specialist Communications. They are all in business to contribute to the success of their clients. And they do so through a demanding combination of flair and slog; intuition and logic; left brain and right brain.

We are looking for people who are intellectually curious and motivated by the prospect of delivering high-quality communications services to their clients. Those selected will work in a number of WPP companies and across different marketing disciplines. Excellent long-term career prospects within a WPP company.

Deadline for entry: 17 November 2009
Visit our website and apply online at www.wpp.com

Information leaflets are available from:
Harriet Miller at WPP, 27 Farm Street,
London W1J 5RJ
T +44(0)20 7408 2204 F +44(0)20 7493 6819
E-mail: hmiller@wpp.com

Enter our prize draw to win

£5,000

or one of a hundred

£50 iTunes vouchers!

Make use of our free information service to find out more about the employers featured within this edition of **The Times Top 100 Graduate Employers,** and you could be £5,000 richer when you start your first job!

All you need to do is complete the special Top 100 **Information Request** card that appears opposite and send it back before the final closing date, **31st March 2010.**

Or you can register your details online at **www.Top100GraduateEmployers.com**

Every completed request card or online registration will be entered into a special prize draw to win £5,000 in cash.

There are also **a hundred £50 iTunes vouchers** to be won – two at <u>each</u> of the universities at which the Top 100 book is distributed, for those who reply by **30th November 2009.**

The information that you request will be dispatched to you from the Top 100 employers directly. This service is entirely free to all UK students and recent graduates.

Fill in the card or go to www.Top100GraduateEmployers.com now!

THE TIMES
TOP 100
GRADUATE EMPLOYERS

INFORMATION REQUEST 2009/2010

To request further information about any of the employers featured in The Times Top 100 Graduate Employers and enter our free prize draw to win £5,000, just complete your details and return this postcard.

Your information will be despatched to you directly from the employers, either by email, post or text message.

NAME

UNIVERSITY

COURSE

TERMTIME ADDRESS

EMAIL

MOBILE TEL. NO.

❑ PRE-FINAL YEAR ❑ FINAL YEAR ❑ I'VE ALREADY GRADUATED

The closing date to request information from these employers and be included in the prize draw to win £5,000 is **Wednesday 31st March 2010.** If you do **not** wish to be included on our general mailing list and receive information from other relevant graduate employers, please tick here ❑

Please tick the sectors that you would most like to work in:

ACCOUNTANCY ❑
CONSULTING ❑
ENGINEERING ❑
FINANCE ❑
GENERAL MANAGEMENT ❑
HUMAN RESOURCES ❑
INVESTMENT BANKING ❑
IT ❑
LAW ❑
LOGISTICS ❑
MANUFACTURING ❑
MARKETING ❑
MEDIA ❑
PURCHASING ❑
RESEARCH & DEVELOPMENT ❑
RETAILING ❑
SALES ❑

Please tick the organisations you would like information from:

ACCENTURE ❑
AIRBUS ❑
ALDI ❑
ALLEN & OVERY ❑
ARCADIA ❑
ARUP ❑
ASDA ❑
ASTRAZENECA ❑
ATKINS ❑
BAE SYSTEMS ❑
BANK OF AMERICA MERRILL LYNCH ❑
BARCLAYS BANK ❑
BARCLAYS CAPITAL ❑
BBC ❑
BDO STOY HAYWARD ❑
BLOOMBERG ❑
BOSTON CONSULTING GROUP ❑
BP ❑
CADBURY ❑
CANCER RESEARCH UK ❑
CITI ❑
CIVIL SERVICE FAST STREAM ❑
CLIFFORD CHANCE ❑
CO-OPERATIVE GROUP ❑
CORUS ❑
CREDIT SUISSE ❑
DELOITTE ❑
DLA PIPER ❑
DSTL ❑
E.ON ❑
EDF ENERGY ❑
ENVIRONMENT AGENCY ❑
ERNST & YOUNG ❑
EXXONMOBIL ❑
FINANCIAL SERVICES AUTHORITY ❑
FRESHFIELDS BRUCKHAUS DERINGER ❑
GCHQ ❑
GLAXOSMITHKLINE ❑
GOLDMAN SACHS ❑
GRANT THORNTON ❑
HSBC ❑

HSBC GLOBAL MARKETS ❑
IBM ❑
J.P. MORGAN ❑
JOHN LEWIS PARTNERSHIP ❑
KPMG ❑
L'ORÉAL ❑
LIDL ❑
LINKLATERS ❑
LLOYDS BANKING GROUP ❑
LOVELLS ❑
MARKS & SPENCER ❑
MARS ❑
McDONALD'S RESTAURANTS ❑
McKINSEY & COMPANY ❑
METASWITCH NETWORKS ❑
METROPOLITAN POLICE ❑
MI5 – THE SECURITY SERVICE ❑
MICROSOFT ❑
MINISTRY OF DEFENCE ❑
MORGAN STANLEY ❑
NETWORK RAIL ❑
NGDP FOR LOCAL GOVERNMENT ❑
NHS ❑
NPOWER ❑
NUCLEARGRADUATES ❑
OXFAM ❑
POLICE HPDS ❑
PRICEWATERHOUSECOOPERS ❑
PROCTER & GAMBLE ❑
QINETIQ ❑
ROLLS-ROYCE ❑
ROYAL BANK OF SCOTLAND GP. ❑
ROYAL NAVY ❑
SAINSBURY'S ❑
SHELL ❑
SIEMENS ❑
SKY ❑
SLAUGHTER AND MAY ❑
TEACH FIRST ❑
TESCO ❑
TRANSPORT FOR LONDON ❑
UBS ❑
UNILEVER ❑
WPP ❑

THE INSTITUTE OF CHARTERED ACCOUNTANTS IN ENGLAND & WALES ❑